DISCIPLESHIP IS A JOURNEY

After baptism, what's next?

A young
believer's guide
to discipleship!

Eleanor P. Hamilton

D1157861

Discipleship Is a Journey has been created to help children understand what comes after accepting Jesus Christ as their Lord and Savior. Its purpose is to teach them how to become a lifelong disciple of Jesus.

Any questions or comments regarding this book, or any other books published by Autumn Light Publications may be directed to publisher@autumnlight.net.

Discipleship Is a Journey
Copyright © 2017 by Eleanor P. Hamilton
Autumn Light Publications
Columbia, MD 21044
ISBN: 978-0-9849797-1-4

Dear Readers,

God offers His gift of Salvation to every person because He wants a restored relationship with EVERYONE. But, each person must decide whether to accept the gift.

Accepting Jesus as Lord and Savior and being baptized in His name seems like a very simple act, but it is actually **a very important decision**, because that one decision affects EVERY decision you make from that point on. That one decision determines WHO will be "in charge" of your life; it is not just a NOW choice, it is a commitment to follow Jesus from NOW ON.

Baptism is only the **beginning** of a lifelong journey with God.

So what comes AFTER baptism? ...**DISCIPLESHIP!**

But, how can you do that?

This simple activity-based study guide has been created to help young believers understand that **Discipleship is an exciting, lifelong journey with Christ**.

Discipleship Is a Journey can be used independently by a young believer to learn how to begin to grow in the Lord, or it can be used as a tool to help a church to implement a mentoring plan for its new young believers.

DISCIPLESHIP IS A JOURNEY

ENTERING DISCIPLESHIP ROAD
Understanding your new role as a Christian

Out with the Old, In with the New (...A review of baptism)
One Driver (...Father, Son, and Holy Spirit are ONE)
Moving In (...Receiving the Holy Spirit)
One Vehicle (...God instituted the Church to share His message)

EQUIPPED FOR DISCIPLESHIP
Understanding and using your resources

One True Word (...The reliability of the Bible)
More Gifts (...The gifts of the Spirit)
Let's Get Together (...Fellowship with the saints)
Direct Line to Heaven (...God hears and answers prayer)

FUELED FOR DISCIPLESHIP
Understanding the role of worship in a Christian's Life

The Heart of Worship (...Not ritual, but genuine dedication)
The Apostle's Doctrine (...Hearing the Word of the Lord)
The Lord's Table (...Why celebrate communion)
It's Not about Money (...Giving offerings to the Lord)

TRAVELING DISCIPLESHIP ROAD
Understanding the role of service in a Christian's life

Not Just a List (...Showing faith by your works)
Growing a Servant's Heart (...Serving others in love)
Not Just Apples and Oranges (...Exhibiting all the fruit of the Spirit)
Cheering Others On (...Encouraging others)

THE ROAD WINDS ON
Understanding that Discipleship is a lifelong journey

Get Back Up (...It's OK to stumble)
Don't Travel Alone (...Sharing your faith with others)
Rough Road Ahead (...Understanding that problems will come)
Don't Close the Book Yet (...Continue learning and growing)

ENTERING DISCIPLESHIP ROAD
Understanding your new role as a Christian

After baptism, a new Christian begins the lifelong journey of living out this new relationship with God. This is called Discipleship. This section reviews some basic concepts a new Christian needs to understand.

Out with the Old, In with the New
(...A review of baptism)

One Driver
(...Father, Son, and Holy Spirit are ONE)

Moving In
(...Receiving the Holy Spirit)

One Vehicle
(...God instituted the Church to share His message)

Out with the Old, In with the New
(...A review of baptism)

II Corinthians 5:17
Therefore if anyone is in Christ, he is a new creature; the old things passed away; behold, new things have come.

Before you begin the journey of Discipleship, let's review the steps that lead to baptism and what actually occurs in the process.

In the beginning God and Man had a wonderful relationship. But, that relationship was ruined **because of SIN**. The only way that special relationship could be restored was for God to fix it. He did that by providing **one way of salvation**. To receive the FREE gift of salvation a person just needs to accept it.

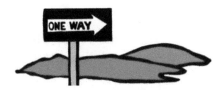

Find the Verse. Complete the blanks:
I am the way, and the truth, and the life. _____ comes to the Father, _____. John 14:6

Why is baptism necessary?

Acts 2:38a explains why baptism is necessary. "Peter said to them, 'Repent, and each of you be baptized in the name of Jesus Christ **for the forgiveness of your sins**."

Unscramble the phrase below to learn why one needs to be baptized

s n o i f g r v e e s
f o   s s n i

That verse is a promise! Whenever a person is baptized in the name of Jesus, his or her sins are forgiven!

What is immersion?

Immerse means to completely submerge, as an object being completely submerged in a body of water. Example: A ship that floats on the ocean is NOT submerged; a ship that has been damaged and begins to sink but is lodged in the sand and rocks along the shore is NOT submerged. But a ship that has completely sunk into the depths of the sea IS submerged.

In the language in which the Bible was written, the verses that refer to the command to be baptized used a word that **literally meant** *to immerse*, or *to submerge.*

Review: What steps lead to the decision to be baptized?

Draw lines matching the steps of God's plan of salvation with a description of each step.

Accept God's plan

Believe Jesus paid for Your Sin

Repent

Confess your Sins

Be Baptized

Be so sorry for your sin that you want to change completely

Be **immersed** in water

Understand that ONLY **God** can restore the broken relationship

Be confident that Jesus died on the cross for **your** sins

Openly admit **you** have sinned

Baptism is a very important step because it means that you are making the decision to let Jesus be in charge of your life from that time on. But what steps led up to that decision?

First, a person must understand what sin is and that it (sin) has broken the relationship between him or her and God. And that person must **ACCEPT** the fact that God alone can restore the relationship and that He has created a plan to do just that.

Second, the person must **BELIEVE** that Jesus died to pay for his or her sin.

Third, the person must **REPENT**, which means that he or she is really sorry for his or her own sins.

Repenting takes place in the person's heart, where no one else can see what is happening. So, the person must then let others know that he or she has repented. To do that, the person must **CONFESS** to others that he or she has repented of his or her sins and that he or she wants to accept God's gift of forgiveness.

Fifth, the person must obey God's command to **BE BAPTIZED** to receive the forgiveness of sins and eternal salvation.

What part do faith, grace, and mercy have in the act of baptism?

Romans 3:23 says that EVERYONE has sinned. Romans 6:23 explains that the only way sin can be paid for is through death. That means that without God's plan everyone would

Find the RED "faith" words from this section in the grid. (Up, down, or diagonal; forward or backward)

Everyone, Death, Sin, Mercy, Grace, Salvation, Gift, Paid, Cross, Faith, Jesus, Confess, Obey, Baptized

B	A	P	C	P	M	E	D	A	T
H	T	I	A	F	G	B	S	E	Y
O	C	I	F	G	R	A	C	E	S
M	D	P	W	Z	H	P	S	N	G
E	S	A	L	V	A	T	I	O	N
R	B	U	D	Q	Y	I	N	Y	D
C	R	Z	S	E	H	Z	L	R	E
Y	R	M	B	E	N	E	F	E	A
J	K	O	C	X	J	D	K	V	T
R	S	C	S	G	I	F	T	E	H
T	Y	S	S	S	E	F	N	O	C

have to pay for their own sin, so they would die spiritually and never get to spend eternity with God.

But, God had mercy on mankind. He did not make us receive what we deserved because of our sin. Instead, He offered His grace. He gave us what we did NOT deserve. He gave us forgiveness.

In God's plan to restore the relationship with mankind, salvation is a free gift. Jesus has already paid the cost of our sin by dying on the cross. All we have to do is accept God's gift. We do that by having faith that God loved us enough to pay the cost. We believe Jesus died for us; we confess and repent of our sins, and we obey His command to be baptized in the name of Jesus.

What is different after baptism?

You are a New Creation!
Just for fun, draw a funny new, unique creature here.

Paul wrote, in II Corinthians 5:17, "Therefore if anyone is in Christ, he is a new creature; the old things have passed away; behold, new things have come." After you accept Jesus as your Savior and are baptized, you are said to be a "new creature."

Though you may not look different, a huge change has occurred inside you. The old *Self*—that part of you that wanted you to be in charge of your life—is now gone. It symbolically *died* and was *buried* when you went down into the waters of baptism. It was your *New Self*—the one that now seeks to let God take charge of your life—that came up out of the water.

What words are applied to the new Christians?

Using 1=A, 2=B, etc. decode
I Peter 2:9a to find more names
Peter used to refer to believers.

25 15 21   1 18 5   1

3 8 15 19 5 14   18 1 3 5,

1   18 15 25 1 12

16 18 9 5 19 20 8 15 15 4,   1

8 15 12 25   14 1 20 9 15 14,

1   16 5 15 16 12 5   6 15 18

7 15 4' 19   15 23 14

16 15 19 19 5 19 19 9 15 14...

When you accepted Christ and was baptized, you became a Christian. There are many other names that the Bible or the Church uses to describe new followers of Christ. Some of the most common names are: **disciple, believer, follower, and child of God.** Because the Christian is in the family of God, the term of **brother or sister** is also frequently used.

In many of his writings, Paul also refers to the believers as **saints.**

Peter, in I Peter 2:9, even provides a much more impressive list of names. You can decode the beginning of that verse to learn the terms he used.

Illustration of Baptism
A caterpillar spins a cocoon and then emerges as a butterfly. The butterfly is often seen as a picture of baptism because the cocoon stage illustrates dying to the old self and the butterfly stage illustrates becoming a NEW CREATURE. Color the butterflies here.

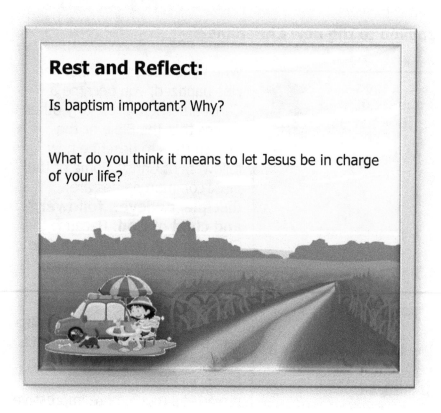

Rest and Reflect:

Is baptism important? Why?

What do you think it means to let Jesus be in charge of your life?

Improving Your Journey

Memorize II Corinthians 5:17.

Begin a Discipleship Bible Study Journal. As you study these lessons write down verses or thoughts that will help you learn to follow Jesus better.

Review your notes often.

One Driver
(...Father, Son, and Holy Spirit are ONE)

John 10:30
I and the Father are One.

Baptism is a very important step in God's plan to restore the relationship that sin destroyed. BUT, it is not an ending; it marks a **beginning**—the beginning of a wonderful journey with your Savior that will last for a lifetime. **That Journey is called Discipleship**.

Remember: **Christian Discipleship** is that relationship which baptism has restored. It is the deep, abiding friendship between God and you. In practice, discipleship is the earnest attempt to become like Christ. It is consciously letting Him be *in charge* of your life. But, what does that really mean? It means that you do everything you can to LEARN what Christ wants you to do AND you do your best to DO it.

Before we consider the marvelous journey that awaits the New Christian, let's first examine just who is involved in it.

Who are the travelers?

You—always remember every step of the journey is **your choice**. God does not want **forced** discipleship.

Circle YES if you want to continue your Discipleship Journey with God.

YES! NO!

Others—your journey and the journeys of other Christians join together as the Church (which will be discussed later), but always remember that the relationship between you and God is **yours alone**. Just as NO ONE could be baptized for you, NO ONE can travel your Discipleship Journey for you.

God—now, here's your key question: Is your NEW relationship with God or with Jesus? **The answer is YES.**

One God, many names

Christians speak of worshipping God, of praying to the Father, of praying in Jesus' name, of accepting Jesus as Lord and Savior, of God being our Lord, of having the Holy Spirit living in us, of Jesus living in us, and more. Sometimes, this can all seem confusing.

So, let's talk about the **One true God** that we worship and serve.

Find the verse. Complete the blanks:
Turn to Me and be _____,
all the ends of the _____;
For I am _____, and there is
_____ _____. Isaiah 45:22

 **WRITE THIS DOWN:**
Write John 10:30.

From the very beginning, God emphasized that He is God—**there is no other**. Exodus 20:3 says, "You shall have no other gods before Me."

We learn from the Bible that Jesus and God are one and the same. In John 10:30, He said, "I and the Father are One." John 14:7 records more of His words, "If you had known Me, you would have known My Father also; from now on you know Him, and have seen Him." Even in one of His earthly names, Emmanuel, we see that Jesus is *God with us.*

Using 1=A, 2=B, etc. decode the meaning of Emmanuel.

7 15 4
23 9 20 8
21 19

In the Scripture we also see another part of God—His Spirit. Romans 8:14 explains that we are "led by the Spirit of God."

What is the Trinity?

Illustration of Trinity
A triangle is composed of 3 sides. Without any one of the sides there is no triangle. In this illustration the triangle represents God. The sides are the Father, Son, and Holy Spirit.

For centuries, Christians have used the term *Trinity* to refer to the difficult idea of One God that interacts with His people through three different ways. Generally, we speak of *three persons* of the trinity—**God the Father, God the Son, and God the Holy Spirit**. Rather than *persons* it may be more accurate to think of the three personalities or offices of God.

The word *trinity* is not found in the Bible, but the first time we see a reference to that idea is in Genesis 1:26, when God says, "Let Us make man in Our image." Use of *us* and *our* shows us that God, speaking of Himself, refers to what we regard as plural—more than one.

Later, God (the heavenly Father) sent His Son (Jesus) to provide salvation for the world. But, Jesus was not a son in the same way that a human boy child is a son to his parents. Jesus was **completely** MAN, and at the same time, **completely** GOD. He even said, "I and the Father are one." It is not something we can fully understand, but Jesus and the Father, Jehovah, are one and the same—**Jesus is God**.

Also, we are told that the **Holy Spirit is God**—that same God, **not a different one**.

Your Discipleship Journey has only ONE Driver!

God is One. He says so and we must believe that it is so. But God interacts with creation in different ways. He is always our heavenly Father. He is also our Savior and

Another Illustration of Trinity
Together three petals make a clover. The petals represent the Father, Son, and Holy Spirit.

Lord (Jesus). And He places His own Spirit (the Holy Spirit) in us when we accept His offer of salvation.

The important thing for new Christians to understand is that whether we speak of Jesus, the heavenly Father, or the Holy Spirit, we are still talking about God. **We serve only ONE God!**

On this wonderful new Journey, the new Christian explores the restored relationship with God that is made possible through the sacrifice of our Lord and Savior, Jesus Christ.

 As you continue this Discipleship Study Guide, you are traveling Discipleship Road with **ONE Driver** by your side!

Build new words!
Write at least 10 words, with at least 4 letters each, using only the letters in the words below.

FATHER SON SPIRIT

Rest and Reflect:

What names for God are most special to you? Why?

What did Jesus mean when He said "if you had known Me, you would have known My Father."?

What is meant by the word *trinity*?

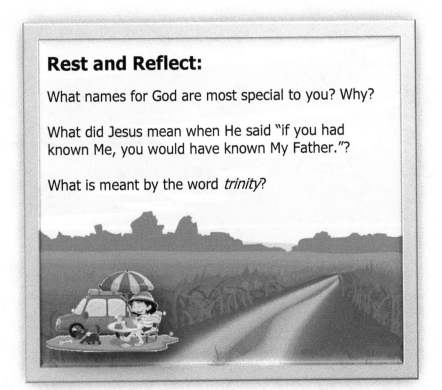

Improving Your Road

Memorize John 14:7.

Write down some of the things you know about God.

Take time to praise God for who He is and what He has done for you.

Moving In
(...Receiving the Holy Spirit)

Acts 2:38
...and you will receive the gift of the Holy Spirit.

A **disciple** is a follower—someone who recognizes the truth and value of another person's teaching and decides to follow in his steps. We are disciples (followers) of Jesus if we, day by day, **follow in His steps**. We make a point to learn what He taught and we try to act in the way that He acted.

BUT, the reality is that in our own strength we cannot do that. That is why God sent someone to help us. **John 14:16** says, "I will ask the Father, and He will give you another Helper, that He may be with you forever." Some translations of this verse use the word *Comforter* instead of *Helper*.

Who is the Holy Spirit?

Who is this Helper or Comforter?

Find the RED "Holy Spirit" words in the grid. (Up, down, or diagonal; forward or backward)

Comforter, Helper, Holy Spirit, Father, God Lord, Jesus Son, Raised, Dead, Christ, Grace

```
E  C  A  R  G  C  M
H  O  L  Y  O  V  T
S  M  W  R  D  D  I
T  F  A  T  H  E  R
S  O  N  O  S  S  I
I  R  M  L  C  I  P
R  T  A  Y  O  A  S
H  E  L  P  E  R  W
C  R  O  D  A  E  D
C  J  E  S  U  S  M
```

He is the Holy Spirit. He is literally the Spirit of God. He is **fully God**, just as **Jesus is fully God**. He is the third part of the **Trinity**.

The Bible calls the Holy Spirit by many names. You can find some of them in the following verses. (These verses refer to wording found in the NASB. Other translations may not provide the exact words listed here.)

John 14:16 (Helper)
John 16:13 (Spirit of truth)
Matthew 1:18 (Holy Spirit)
Matthew 10:20 (Spirit of your Father)
I Corinthians 2:11 (Spirit of God)
Acts 5:9 (Spirit of the Lord)
Acts 8:29 (the Spirit)
Acts 16:7 (Spirit of Jesus)
Galatians 4:6 (Spirit of His Son)
Romans 8:11 (Spirit of Him who raised Jesus from the dead)
Ephesians 3:16 (His Spirit)
Philippians 1:19 (Spirit of Jesus Christ)
Hebrews 10:29 (Spirit of grace)

Beyond those names given directly in the Scripture, Christians also sometimes speak of God's Spirit and Christ's Spirit, and we understand that all of these names refer to the **Holy Spirit of God**.

> Using 1=A, 2=B, etc. decode II Corinthians 5:17 to see Paul's reference to a "new creature."
>
> 20 8 5 18 5 6 15 18 5   9 6
>
> 1 14 25 15 14 5   9 19   9 14
>
> 3 8 18 9 19 20,   8 5   9 19
>
> 1   14 5 23   3 18 5 1 20 21 18 5;
>
> 20 8 5   15 12 4   20 8 9 14 7 19
>
> 16 1 19 19 5 4   1 23 1 25;
>
> 2 5 8 15 12 4   14 5 23
>
> 20 8 9 14 7 19   8 1 22 5
>
> 3 15 13 5.

How do we receive the Holy Spirit?

For a moment think back to your baptism. Through baptism, **sins are washed away**. They are gone, **completely**! That's how you can be, as Paul says in II Corinthians 5:17, *a new creature*. The OLD SELF is gone. When you came up out of the waters of baptism, you were a new creature, a NEW CREATION!

You did not look different (other than being completely soaked), but you are different. Because, with the washing away of sins, you received a **bonus**! Remember Acts 2:38. Peter said, "Repent. Be baptized. AND **you will receive** the gift of the Holy Spirit." That means that a part of that wonderful gift of salvation **includes** the presence of the Holy Spirit coming to be with you always.

Unscramble the different gifts that are included with salvation.

t e e a n l r   i l e f
s n r o g f i e v e s
y o H l   i S r t p i

Remember Matthew 28:20 where Jesus promised to be with you **always**. THIS is how He does it. As the Holy Spirit, Jesus IS with us every moment of every day!

Baptism did not just wash away all the sin that stained your life, it made it possible for the Holy Spirit of God to **come into your life**. That is why Paul could say in Galatians 2:20 that he no longer lived, but that Jesus lived in him.

What does the Holy Spirit do?

How much does the Holy Spirit weigh?

We can't see or touch the Holy Spirit. We cannot feel the physical weight of His presence in our lives. We cannot describe what He looks like; we can only describe what He does.

Jesus told His disciples why He would have the Father send the Helper. In John 14:26, Jesus said, "But the Helper, the Holy Spirit, whom the Father will send in My name, He will **teach you all things**, and **bring to your remembrance** all that I said to you."

WRITE THIS DOWN:
Write down the two things the Holy Spirit will do for you.

So the Holy Spirit's primary job in our lives is to **teach us** and to **help us remember** what we have already been taught. That means He helps us to learn and understand the Word of God and once we have learned from the Word, He helps us to remember it so we can make use of it in our lives.

Take Note: This is not an instant memory trick! You will have to make the effort to study and learn, but the Holy Spirit will help you.

Now, let's look at some other things the Holy Spirit does in our lives. Look up the verses below and match them to the work that the Holy Spirit does.

Draw lines matching the verses with a description of what the Holy Spirit does to help the believer.

Ephesians 6:22	Helps us pray
Romans 15:13	Helps guard our "treasure"
Romans 8:26	Comforts us
II Timothy 1:14	Guides our decisions
Acts 13:4 and 16:6	Helps fill us with hope

REMEMBER: God did not force us to accept His gift of salvation. He also does not force us to follow Him. The Holy Spirit is with us to help, but **we always have the choice** of whether to pay attention to what He tries to teach us. We are not puppets; we follow God by choice.

Rest and Reflect:

Since we cannot see the Holy Spirit, how can we know that He lives inside us?

Name some times you feel that the Holy Spirit has helped you.

How does the Holy Spirit help you become a better disciple?

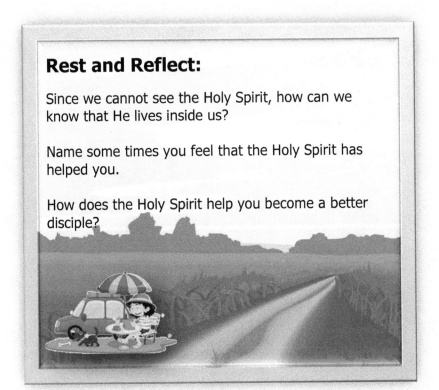

Improving Your Road

Memorize John 14:26.

Write down some of the ways the Holy Spirit helps you.

Thank God for sending the Holy Spirit to come live inside you.

One Vehicle
(...God instituted the Church to share His message)

Matthew 28:19
Go therefore and make disciples of all the nations, baptizing them in the name of the Father and the Son and the Holy Spirit, teaching them to observe all that I commanded you; and lo, I am with you always, even to the end of the age.

As you begin your journey it is important that you realize that you are not traveling alone—not entirely. Your journey is yours alone, but God has made a way for you to have others share the experience.

STOP

WRITE THIS DOWN:
If you believe it, write out the Good Confession.

What is the Church?

According to the dictionary, a ***church*** is 1) a building used for Christian religious services, 2) the religious services held in the church building, or 3) a particular Christian group.

All of these definitions are correct, but NONE of them fully describe the *Church* as God designed it to be.

What then is the Church? When Jesus asked His disciples who they believed Him to be, Peter responded, "You are the Christ, the Son of the living God." Jesus then said, "On this rock [the statement that Peter had made], **I will build my Church.**" (Matthew 16: 15-18)

Peter's statement is often called the **good confession**. It is the basic statement of faith that many people declare when they make the decision to accept Jesus as Lord and Savior and to follow Him in baptism. In that statement is Christ's basic definition of the Church: **all people who recognize that Jesus is God's Son and claim His gift of salvation through baptism**.

When and how did the Church begin?

Thousands of people gathered in Jerusalem every year for the Feast of Weeks, or Pentecost. Pentecost was a joyful celebration of the harvest season that occurred fifty days after Passover each year.

Find the words below in the grid below. Words may be up, down, or diagonal. They may also be spelled forward or backward.

Places of Worship

```
A  E  C  A  T  H  E  D  R  A  L
B  L  G  O  D  S  H  O  U  S  E
A  C  I  L  I  S  A  B  Q  U  L
E  A  C  H  U  R  C  H  G  S  P
G  N  N  E  U  Q  S  O  M  H  M
I  R  H  Y  D  Q  G  Y  C  R  E
N  E  S  C  H  A  P  E  L  I  T
F  B  K  Z  N  J  F  B  S  N  W
R  A  K  Y  H  D  J  B  I  E  H
I  T  S  A  D  O  G  A  P  O  W
```

ABBEY	CURCH	SHRINE
BASILICA	GOD'S HOUSE	SYNAGOGUE
CATHEDRAL	MOSQUE	TABERNACLE
CHAPEL	PAGODA	TEMPLE

In the year of Christ's death and resurrection, approximately 30 AD, the **Day of Pentecost** took on a new significance. On that day, Christ's Church began.

Before Jesus ascended into heaven, He told His disciples to wait in Jerusalem until the Father sent the promised Comforter, the Holy Spirit.

Acts 2 describes the coming of the Holy Spirit. The Bible says that a noise came from heaven like a violent rushing wind that filled the whole house where the disciples were gathered. Tongues of fire rested on each of the disciples. As the Holy Spirit filled the disciples they received power from God to speak in languages they had not known before, power to heal, and power to perform miracles.

Peter, through the power of the Holy Spirit, stood up and preached. He told the mass of people about Jesus—about His life, His death, and His resurrection. More than 3,000 people believed what Peter told them. They accepted Jesus as their Lord and were baptized in His name.

That was the beginning of the **Church**.

What is the primary job of the Church?

Matthew 28:19 explains the work that He left for the disciples to do. Simply put, they were to **Go**, **make** disciples, **teach** those disciples to obey Christ's commands, and **baptize** new believers.

In other words the primary job of the Church is to **tell others about Jesus** so more people can accept Him.

Who is the head of the Church?

Build new words!
Write at least 10 words, with at least 4 letters each, using only the letters in the word below.

PENTECOST

Jesus is the head of the Church (See Colossians 1:18 and Ephesians 1:22). Before He ascended, He prepared His disciples to lead the Church. After He ascended, the Father sent the Holy Spirit to help the new believers accomplish the job they had been given.

Jesus left the apostles on earth to begin the work of the Church. They, in turn, left other church leaders to direct the Church. **Elders** were chosen to help guide the small congregations of believers and **deacons** were chosen to help serve the physical needs of the people.

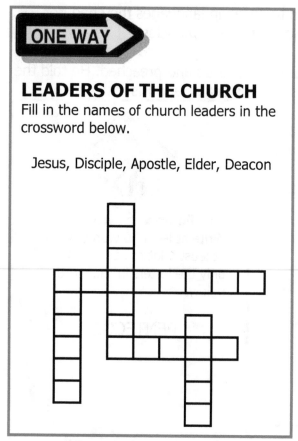

LEADERS OF THE CHURCH

Fill in the names of church leaders in the crossword below.

Jesus, Disciple, Apostle, Elder, Deacon

On earth the governing of the Church was left to the apostles and later to the elders, who were led by the Holy Spirit. But then, and now, Jesus remains the **founder** and the **head of the Church**. That will never change.

What is Christ's desire for the Church?

Jesus wants His Church to be **unified**. Jesus knew that as the Church grew, disagreements would threaten to tear it apart. Even before He died, Jesus prayed for His disciples, asking the Father to make them One even as We [Jesus and the Father] are One (John 17:11, 21-22).

Paul in I Corinthians 1:10 also urged the Church to be united. He appealed to believers to "agree with one another" and to be "perfectly united in mind and thought."

What are some other names for the Church?

Body of Christ

Paul's letters often refers to the Church as the Body of Christ. I Corinthians 12:12 says, "For even as the body [a physical body] is one and yet has many members, and all the members of the body, though they are many, are one body, so also is Christ."

Unscramble the letters to find what Jesus most wanted for His Church.

t n i u y

Paul's comparison emphasizes that the Church is made up of many people, but all the believers in Christ together form the **body of Christ** here on earth.

Bride of Christ

The Church is also referred to as the **bride of Christ**. The book of Revelation describes the reunion of Christ and the Church by referring to the "marriage of the Lamb."

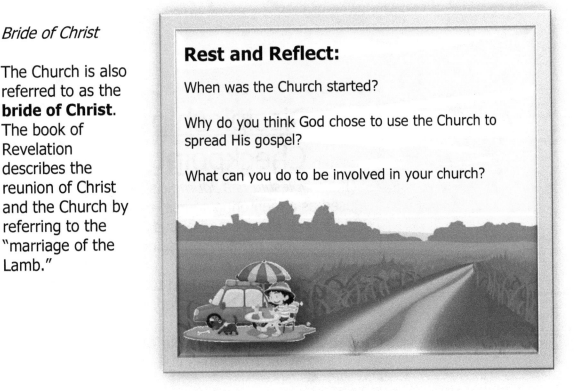

Rest and Reflect:

When was the Church started?

Why do you think God chose to use the Church to spread His gospel?

What can you do to be involved in your church?

Improving Your Road

Memorize Matthew 28:19.

Pray for the leaders of your church.

Make a Thank-you card or write a letter for one of your leaders.

Discipleship Checkpoint

(If *Discipleship Is a Journey* is being used as a mentoring course, review the 4 prior lessons and discuss them with your mentor/counselor.)

Describe the steps that led to your decision to be baptized.

Describe to the best of your ability what *trinity* means.

Why did God send the Holy Spirit to live inside you?

What does being part of Christ's Church mean to you?

EQUIPPED FOR DISCIPLESHIP
Understanding and using your resources

God provides new Christians with some basic resources. If we understand that we have access to these resources, following His will is easier. This section reviews some of those basic resources that are available to you.

One True Word
(...The reliability of the Bible)

More Gifts
(...The gifts of the Spirit)

Let's Get Together
(...Fellowship with the saints)

Direct Line to Heaven
(...God hears and answers prayer)

One True Word
(...The reliability of the Bible)

II Timothy 3:16-17
All Scripture is inspired by God and profitable for teaching, for reproof, for correction, for training in righteousness; so that the man of God may be adequate, equipped for every good work.

One of the greatest resources available to the Christian is the Bible—**the Word of God**. Every Christian needs to understand that the Bible is the true, inspired Word of God. Everything in the Bible can be trusted because the One who inspired it can be trusted.

How is the Bible content organized?

The Bible is a collection of **66 books**, written over the span of about a thousand years, by a variety of writers.

The Bible has **2 major divisions.** We call these Old Testament and New Testament. These names refer to the Covenants (or agreements) that exist between God and His people.

Under the old covenant God promised Abraham that He would make a great nation from his descendants. He did that through the nation of Israel. The Old Testament is the history of the Jewish people, as He **prepared them for the Messiah** who would one day come to restore the relationship that sin had destroyed.

Under the new covenant, God promises eternal life that is made possible through the sacrifice of Jesus on the cross. The New Testament is the story of the time Jesus was here on earth and a **guidebook of how we are to live** while we wait for His return.

The Old Testament has 39 books that are separated into 5 different categories: 5 Books of Law (Genesis – Deuteronomy); 12 Books of History (Joshua – Esther); 5 Books of Poetry (Job – Song of Solomon); 5 Books of Major Prophets (Isaiah – Daniel); 12 Books of Minor Prophets (Hosea – Malachi).

Major and *Minor* refer to the length of the books, not to their importance.

The New Testament has 27 books that are separated into 4 different categories: 4 Books called the Gospels (Matthew – John); 1 Book of History (Acts); 21 Books of Apostles' Letters (Romans – Jude); and 1 Book of Prophecy (Revelation).

Find the Bible books listed below in the grid. Words may be up, down, or diagonal. They may also be spelled forward or backward.

BIBLE BOOKS

```
P  E  S  A  M  U  E  L  H  T
E  J  L  E  O  J  E  T  S  R
J  O  W  O  K  I  U  D  E  T
H  S  B  E  N  R  S  I  M  I
A  H  L  A  H  S  O  M  A  M
N  U  D  U  D  T  E  I  J  O
O  A  W  P  K  I  T  C  J  T
J  M  A  R  K  E  A  A  D  H
E  Z  E  K  I  E  L  H  M  Y
```

Amos, Daniel, Ezekiel, James, Joel, Jonah, Joshua, Luke, Mark, Matthew, Micah, Obadiah, Ruth, Samuel, Timothy

WRITE THIS DOWN:
Who is the Author of the Bible?

Where did the Bible come from?

The Bible is the Written Word of God. II Timothy 3:15-17 explains that the Bible was *inspired by God,* or *God-breathed.* This means that it is God's words that appear in the Bible. Though many writers were used to produce the Bible, **God is its author!** God chose a variety of people to write the Bible, but, through the Holy Spirit, He guided their thoughts

Unscramble the categories of Old Testament Books.

a l w
y e p t o r

y o i h t s r
t r p o p e h s

Unscramble the categories of New Testament Books.

s e p g l s o
r t l s e t e

o y i r h t s
c r y h p p o e

and understanding to be able to put down the actual printed text that He wanted us to have.

The first books of the Old Testament (the Books of Law) were probably written down in the late 1400's BC and the last one (Malachi) was written about 450 BC. The New Testament books were written from about 45 AD to 95 AD. Thus more than **a thousand years** was required to actually complete the writing of the Bible.

How did God communicate with His people before the Bible was written?

Before the Written Word of God was given, God communicated through prophets. Now, we have the Bible to give us the instructions of God. God Himself provided the Written Word for us (Hebrews 1:1-2).

What is the language used to produce the Bible?

The Old Testament was originally written mostly in **Hebrew**; the New Testament was originally written mostly in **Greek**.

But mankind needs to have the scripture in their native language to

Using 1=A, 2=B, etc. to decode Matthew 24:35, another reminder about God's Word.

8 5 1 22 5 14   1 14 4

5 1 18 20 8   23 9 12 12

16 1 19 19   1 23 1 25,

2 21 20   13 25

23 15 18 4 19   23 9 12 12

14 15 20   16 1 19 19

1 23 1 25.

fully understand it. For that reason, the Bible has been translated into many languages. Any translation that **accurately** translates the full text and intention of the scripture can be used to study the Word of God.

What proof do we have that God's Word is STILL the same?

Isaiah 40:8 reminds us, "The grass withers and the flowers fall, but the word of our God stands forever." Just as God very carefully made sure that the Bible contained His words when it was written, He also protected it through the thousands of years since.

In the last few centuries ancient copies have been found of both the Old and the New Testaments. By comparing those texts with our current translations, we can be assured that our Bible is STILL the accurate, unchanged Word of God.

Examples of such discoveries:

Late in 1859 AD, Constantine Tischendorf found an ancient copy of the New Testament at St. Catherine's Monastery. That copy is believed to have been produced around 350 AD. Scribes at that time would have used an older manuscript and carefully copied the words to produce the one that was found in 1859. This copy of the New Testament is referred to as Codex (meaning book) Sinaiticus.

Build new words!
Write at least 10 words, with at least 4 letters each, using only the letters in the words below.

DEAD SEA SCROLLS

In 1947, a young Bedouin goat herder accidentally discovered a treasure of ancient scrolls in the caves around the Dead Sea. The Old Testament Scripture on some of the Dead Sea Scrolls were probably recorded as early as 100 BC.

Rest and Reflect:

Who is the author of the Bible?

Describe the breakdown of the books of the Bible.

How can we be sure the Bible we have now is accurate?

Improving Your Road

Memorize II Timothy 3:16-17.

Memorize the Books of the Bible.

Learning the order of the books will help you find passages more quickly.

More Gifts
(...The gifts of the Spirit)

I Corinthians 12: 7, 11
But to each one is given the manifestation of the Spirit for the common good...
But one and the same Spirit works all these things, distributing to each one
individually just as He wills.

On the Day of Pentecost, the Holy Spirit came to dwell in the apostles. He gave them powerful **spiritual gifts** that helped them establish the Church. Thorough the power of the Holy Spirit, Peter, a simple fisherman from Galilee, became a preacher who reached more than 3000 people with his first sermon. Peter and John, through the power of the Spirit, were able to heal the sick and perform other miracles.

The *Gifts of the Spirit* made it possible for the apostles to know what they needed to know in order to do the things that would make the Church strong.

Is the gift of the Holy Spirit and the gifts of the Spirit the same?

No.

Remember Acts 2:38. When you believe in Jesus and are baptized, you also receive the *gift of the Holy Spirit*. This is a **bonus gift** from God— forgiveness of your sins **AND** the gift of the Holy Spirit. We learned earlier that the Holy Spirit is given to new Christians

> Unscramble the phrase below to learn what you received when you were baptized.
>
> 1. e n o s r v f i g e s
> 2. l o H y i i p S r t

to help them to continue to grow in their new relationship with Jesus.

Now, here's **ANOTHER bonus**! The Holy Spirit also has special gifts that He gives to every believer. These gifts are sometimes called **spiritual gifts**. The Holy Spirit gives new Christians His gifts, so that new Christian can edify (build up) the Church.

Are the gifts of the Spirit the same as the fruit of the Spirit?

No. The fruit of the Spirit will be the subject of a later section.

Are the gifts of the Spirit the same as God-given talents?

Again, no.

Many of the gifts of the Spirit are much like natural talents that came to you from God. You may have been born with the ability to be an effective teacher or you may have a very logical mind that makes administration tasks come easy. The gifts of the Spirt go deeper, providing qualities that go beyond normal circumstance. His gifts are exclusively given to believers **for the purpose of serving the Church**.

Using 1=A, 2=B, etc. decode I Corinthians 14:12b to learn why the Spirit gives special gifts.

19 5 5 11   20 15

1 2 15 21 14 4   6 15 18

20 8 5   5 4 9 6 9 3 1 20 9 15 14

15 6   20 8 5   3 8 21 18 3 8

What are the gifts of the Spirit?

There are a lot of different gifts of the Spirit mentioned in the Bible. Romans 12, I Corinthians 12, and Ephesians 4 mention one or more of the following gifts: *administration, apostle, discernment, evangelism, exhortation, faith, giving, healings, helps, knowledge, leadership, mercy, miracles, pastor, prophecy, service, teaching, tongues, tongues interpretation, and wisdom.*

In I Corinthians 12:11 Paul emphasized that gifts of the Spirit were given individually to the believers, **as He (the Spirit) chose**. Not everyone received the same gift, or even the same number of gifts. We do not have a say in what gifts we receive from the Spirit.

Remember: The purpose of the gifts is to **edify or build up the Church** (I Corinthians 14:12), not to bring honor to the individual believer.

Simple definitions...

Many of the gifts of the Spirit are difficult for a young Christian to understand, but here is a basic list of simple definitions:

Administration	ability to direct the operation of the church
Apostleship	ability to begin and oversee new churches
Discernment	ability to recognize truth from error
Evangelism	ability to effectively lead unbelievers to Christ
Exhortation	ability to motivate others to grow in the Lord
Faith	ability to confidently believe God's vision will be accomplished
Giving	ability to contribute material resources cheerfully & with generosity
Healings	ability to serve as an instrument God can use to heal another
Helps	ability to enhance the effectiveness of the ministry
Knowledge	ability to discover and analyze information
Leadership	ability to delegate tasks & motivate others to complete the tasks
Mercy	ability to deeply empathize with those who are suffering
Miracles	ability to serve as an instrument God uses to do supernatural works

Pastor	ability to personal lead, nourish, protect, and care for the people
Prophecy	ability to provide a message from God to a specific group
Service	ability to identify and care for the physical needs of the Church
Teaching	ability to clearly explain and apply God's Word so other can learn it
Tongues	ability to receive and give messages in a language never learned
Tongues, interpretation	ability to translate a message in tongues
Wisdom	ability to apply God's Word in practical ways

Are all the gifts of the Spirit still seen in our churches today?

In I Corinthians 13:8 Paul said, "Love never fails; but if there are gifts of prophecy, they will be done away; if there are tongues, they will cease; if there is knowledge, it will be done away." Paul was emphasizing the fact that the Spirit gives His gifts **when they are needed** for the survival of the Church, and explains that not every one of the gifts may be needed at any given time.

Some of the gifts of the Spirit are not seen in churches today in the same way they were in the early years of the Church. The Church does not require the gift of prophecy because **the full, complete Word of God is in our hands**. The gifts of tongues and knowledge are generally associated with the need to understand God's will and His purpose; these again are needed less now that the written Word of God is in our hands.

Remember: the gifts of the Holy Spirit were (and are) for the purpose of building up the Church—providing any skill it needs to continue on into the next generation. Whatever special skills or powers are needed in any generation for the Church to survive and stay strong, the Holy Spirit will provide. The fact that a particular gift of the Spirit is not evident today, in no way means that the Holy Spirit can no longer provide it, if it is again needed.

Young Christian, take note:

As a young believer, you may not yet recognize your special spiritual gift. Remember that its **purpose is to build up the church** and you are not in a position to help govern the church yet.

For now, know that the Holy

Spirit has assigned to you one or more spiritual gifts to be used to build up the Church. Right now, those gifts are still being developed in you.

As your journey continues and you become a more mature part of the Church, He (the Holy Spirit) will begin to reveal those gifts to you.

Rest and Reflect:

Why does the Holy Spirit give special gifts to believers?

Are gifts of the Spirit and fruit of the Spirit the same thing?

Name a few of the gifts of the Spirit.

Improving Your Road

Memorize I Corinthians 12:11.

Look over the list of special gifts the Holy Spirit gives. Remember that the purpose of the gifts is to build up the Church—to make the Church more effective in doing God's will. What 2-3 gifts do you think the Spirit may have given you? What could you do now to help you be ready to use those gifts for the Lord?

ROAD CONSTRUCTION GUIDE

Let's Get Together
(...Fellowship with the saints)

Hebrews 10:25a
Not forsaking our own assembling together, as is the habit of some, but encouraging one another

The early Christians understood that it was necessary to get together often to find strength and encouragement. Hebrews 10:25 even instructed them to not stop assembling (meeting) together.

Ecclesiastes 4:9-12 gives us a wonderful illustration. The passage is describing **why** two are better than one, comparing the strength and safety of two people together to a cord, saying a single strand is broken easily but a cord of many strands is very strong and more difficult to break. The same is true of Christians. If one Christian tries to stand against temptation alone, he is likely to fall; but if many Christians support one another, they can all stand against temptation and remain faithful.

Build new words!
Write at least 10 words, with at least 4 letters each, using only the letters in the word below.

FELLOWSHIP

What is Fellowship?

Fellowship is the gathering together for the purpose of sharing similar interests. It involves interaction between people who have something in common.

Fellowship among Christians is a key factor. They encourage one another to remain faithful and they share what they know about the Lord, helping one another to grow in **knowledge** of God's Word and in **experience** in living for Him.

Fellowship includes going to church.

When the Church first began, the people made a practice of gathering together EVERY week, on the first day of the week. They met every week because they understood their need to be with people who shared their belief that Jesus was (and is) the promised Messiah.

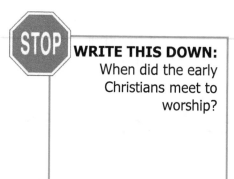

WRITE THIS DOWN: When did the early Christians meet to worship?

Fellowship does not only mean going to church.

The church (the regular meeting place of believers) is a great place to find opportunities to build friendships. Remember Hebrews 10:25. Christians are supposed to meet together regularly.

However, church is not the only place that Christians can meet together. The Bible tells us that wherever two or more gather in His name, Jesus is there with them (Matthew 18:20).

The key that makes fellowship become **Christian Fellowship** is not the place, but the people involved and the purpose for which they are meeting. Christians need to be friends with other Christians. Christians need to spend time with other Christians.

So, do we need to go to church regularly?

Absolutely! As their lives get busier, Christians are sometimes tempted to skip church once in a while. Sometimes they even get out of the practice of going to church at all.

Sometimes, they even forget that the act of meeting together with other Christians is one of the most valuable resources that God gave us. **Regularly** attending church together and sharing fellowship with other believers should be **a high priority in our schedules**.

Never forget Hebrews 10:25. *Going to church* is not a burden that is placed on the Christian. It is special resource God has provided to help Christians stay faithful and grow a deeper relationship with Him.

Rest and Reflect:

What is the difference between Fellowship and Christian Fellowship?

What are ways you might fellowship with other believers?

Why should you go to church regularly?

Improving Your Road

Memorize Hebrews 10:25.

What are some reasons that you may not be able to go to church?

What could you do in those circumstances to still stay connected to your church?

Direct Line to Heaven
(...God hears and answers prayer)

Colossians 4:2
"Devote yourselves to prayer, keeping alert in it with an attitude of thanksgiving."

Another resource that is provided to all of God's followers is prayer—the direct line of communication with our heavenly Father.

What is prayer?

Prayer is an eternal—always open—connection to God. When we pray, we are communicating with our heavenly Father.

Prayer is sometimes intended to be a communication on behalf of a group of people, like prayers that are included in our worship services. In that situation, the one who is praying is representing the whole congregation.

Most prayer, though, is personal. It is direct conversation between you and God. Remember, even though Jesus is your Savior and King, He is also your Friend. He wants you to take time to talk with Him.

Do I have to kneel and close my eyes?

The Bible never says that we must kneel, or that we must close our eyes. There is no instruction saying that you must say your prayer

Using 1=A, 2=B, etc. decode Acts 6:4 for another message from the early church about prayer.

2 21 20   23 5   23 9 12 12

4 5 22 15 20 5

15 21 18 19 5 12 22 5 19   20 15

16 18 1 25 5 18   1 14 4

20 15   20 8 5

13 9 14 9 19 20 18 25   15 6

20 8 5   23 15 18 4.

aloud and there is no command to place your hands together in the manner that is seen in the typical *praying hands* picture.

Why should I pray? Doesn't He already know what I need?

Remember: **Discipleship is all about relationship**—living out our friendship with our Lord. Communication is a part of that friendship. We pray just because we want to talk to our Friend. Through prayer, we spend time with God, and the more time we spend with Him the more we are able to grow to be like Him.

Beyond that, we pray because God wants us to do it. He wants us to choose to spend time with Him. There's that word again—Prayer is a **choice**!

Colossians 4:2 tells us to "Devote yourselves to prayer, keeping alert in it with an attitude of thanksgiving."

I Thessalonians 3:10 tells us to "pray without ceasing."

Are there different kinds of prayer?

Prayer may involve a lot of different kinds of conversations with our Lord. He wants you to come to Him with all your needs and concerns. I Peter 5:7 tells us to "cast all our anxiety on Him," meaning that you can take anything that concerns you to Him because He cares about you. So, what kind of things might you include in your conversations with God?

Petition – ASK for what you need. (It's ok to ask for what you *want*, too. But always remember you are striving to only *want* what is a part of His will for your life.)

Confession— ADMIT wrongs you have done. (Also, ask for forgiveness and truly strive to not ever do the wrong again.)

Intercession— ASK for what others need. (Ask for their physical needs and for their spiritual needs. Remember that what your friends need most is to know Jesus.)

Thanksgiving— APPRECIATE everything He has done for you and tell Him that you do.

Praise—ACKNOWLEDGE who He is.

Is thanksgiving and praise the same concept?

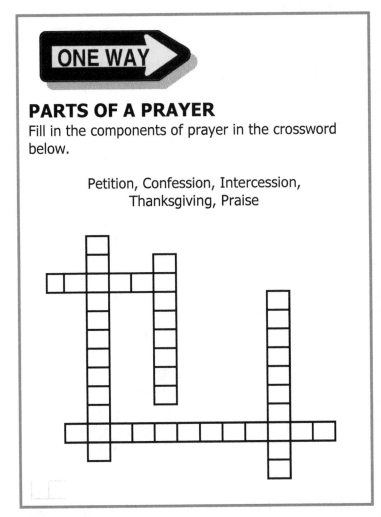

PARTS OF A PRAYER
Fill in the components of prayer in the crossword below.

Petition, Confession, Intercession, Thanksgiving, Praise

Before we move on, let's look at Thanksgiving and Praise. Sometimes the two look very much alike—we praise God for what He has given us. Still, there is a difference that you should understand.

Thanksgiving is about acknowledging what God has done for you. **Praise** is about acknowledging who God is and what He has done, just because He is God. The subtle difference comes in the fact that with thanksgiving it is partially about us, in praise it is ALL about Him. Both are vital parts of our prayer life.

How should I pray?

The Disciples asked Jesus that same question. He gave them a model prayer that is found in what we call *the Lord's Prayer*.

Find the words below in the grid. Words may be up, down, or diagonal. They may also be spelled forward or backward.

LORD'S PRAYER

```
L  D  R  E  V  I  G  R  O  F
R  E  E  E  G  T  E  M  A  N
E  L  P  W  L  D  A  I  L  Y
W  I  F  M  O  D  G  N  I  K
O  V  O  A  R  L  T  H  Y  R
P  E  R  S  Y  H  L  E  E  E
B  R  E  A  D  L  Z  A  M  H
W  E  V  M  I  N  R  V  H  T
A  M  E  W  H  T  G  E  U  A
Y  N  R  S  H  J  G  N  R  F
```

Bread	Father	Hallowed	Power
Daily	Forever	Heaven	Will
Deliver	Forgive	Kingdom	
Earth	Glory	Name	

Let's look at the model found in Matthew 6:9-13: Jesus said, "Pray, then, in this way:

Praise

'Our Father who is in heaven, Hallowed be Your name.'

Hallowed means *honored* or *holy*. You should begin your prayer by reverently letting God know that you **understand** just how holy He is and you **want** to honor Him.

Petition

'Your kingdom come. Your will be done, on earth as it is in heaven.'

You should then surrender (give up) your own will and let God know that you really want His will to be done here on earth. This means that you are telling God again that you **choose** to let Him to be the King of your life.

Petition, Thanksgiving

'Give us this day our daily bread.'
As you pray, you are telling God you understand that **He supplies** all your needs, and that you are asking Him for the things you think you need right now.

Petition, Confession

'And forgive us our debts, as we also have forgiven our debtors.'
In this part of the prayer model you are asking God to forgive the sins that you commit. But you are also admitting that because you know you are forgiven you also know that you must **choose** to show that same kind of forgiveness to others.

Petition, Intercession

'And do not lead us into temptation, but deliver us from evil.'
We know there is always temptation to do wrong, so as you pray, you are to ask God to help you avoid the temptations so you can avoid sinning again. In this part of your prayer you are **choosing** again to accept God's definition of right and wrong and you are **choosing** to try to only do what He says is right.

Praise

'[For Yours is the kingdom and the power and the glory forever. Amen']

STOP

WRITE THIS DOWN:
Write some types of things that you could pray for.

Some translations leave this last line out of the text, because it was missing from a couple of the ancient manuscripts that were found. Other translations of the Bible include it because it was included in many of the other manuscripts that have been found. There are very few of these circumstances in the Bible, but when they occur the situation is usually marked by using brackets [ ] around the words.

In the model prayer, Jesus instructed His disciples to close their prayers as they had started them, by honoring God. Notice that the model prayer starts and ends with PRAISE. Never forget that though He wants a personal relationship with you, He is still Almighty God and worthy of all praise and worship!

Rest and Reflect:

Describe the various types of prayers that you can include in your conversation with the Lord. Give examples of each.

Describe the difference between Thanksgiving and Praise.

Improving Your Road

Memorize Colossians 4:2.

Memorize the different types of prayers.

Try to include all the different types of prayer in your communications with God, but sometimes make a point to just go to Him with praise and thanksgiving.

Discipleship Checkpoint

(If *Discipleship Is a Journey* is being used as a mentoring course, review the 4 prior lessons and discuss them with your mentor/counselor.)

Who is the author of the Bible? Why can we be sure it is still the same as when God inspired the writers to write it?

Are the gift of the Spirit and Spiritual Gifts the same? What is the difference?

What is the difference between Fellowship and Christian Fellowship? Why is going to church important?

Describe what prayer means. What might it include?

FUELED FOR DISCIPLESHIP
Understanding the role of worship in a Christian's Life

Early Christians learned that choosing certain practices strengthened their continuing relationship with the Lord. This section reviews some of those basic practices that will also help you to strengthen your relationship with God.

 The Heart of Worship
(...Not ritual, but genuine dedication)

 The Apostle's Doctrine
(...Hearing the Word of the Lord)

 The Lord's Table
(...Why celebrate communion)

 It's Not about Money
(...Giving offerings to the Lord)

The Heart of Worship
(...Not ritual, but genuine dedication)

Psalm 29:2
Ascribe to the LORD the glory due to His name; Worship the LORD in holy array.
John 4:24
God is spirit, and those who worship Him must worship in spirit and truth.

Worship is an expression of reverence and adoration. It is showing respect to the One who is worthy of all honor and praise, just because of **Who** He is. It is not only the acts that are done to communicate our love and thankfulness, it is the deep dedication in our heart that overflows and spills out through those actions.

Is worship just going to church on Sunday?

As Christians we come together to worship God on Sundays. That does not mean that Sunday is the only time we worship God, but it is a specific time when God's people come together in shared worship.

Find the Verse. Complete the blanks:

_____ the Lord with
_____ and
rejoice with _____.
Psalm 2:11

Do I need to be with others to worship?

Yes, sometimes, AND No, sometimes. Worship is a matter of the Heart—it is our personal expression of our reverence and our love. Sometimes that is a private experience between you and God, but other times it needs to be shared, so the combined worship of all the believers can be presented to God.

Is Worship an action or a relationship?

Worship is the condition of your heart—it is defined by the priority that you place on your relationship with God. But, the **evidence** of that worship is all the various ways that our bodies and mind use to show God how much He means to us.

John said we must worship the Lord in spirit and in truth. God takes no delight in rituals or gifts that are just for show, but He is very pleased with ANY act (great or small) that is done out of true love for Him.

Many people feel that stained glass windows, like the one shown here, inspire them to worship.

Color the stained glass window as a part of your own worship of the Lord.

What are rituals?

A ritual is a solemn ceremony that includes several actions that are done in a precise order and manner. Rituals begin with a clear, honorable purpose, but if the heart is not right, they can become just empty actions. Those are the *rituals* that God takes no delight in. His objection would be not to the action itself but rather to the fact that someone was performing it only for show, not out of love for Him.

Mark records in Mark 7:6: "And He said to them, 'Rightly did Isaiah prophesy of you hypocrites, as it is written: THIS PEOPLE HONORS ME WITH THEIR LIPS, BUT THEIR HEART IS FAR AWAY FROM ME.'" The Jews that Mark spoke about did all the right things to look like they were worshiping God, but their hearts did not truly worship Him.

What are specific acts of worship?

Psalm 100:1-5 provides many outward expressions of the dedication and reverence in our hearts.

Serve the Lord with gladness—service with a willing attitude is an act of worship.

Find the RED "worship" words in the grid. (Up, down, or diagonal; forward or backward)

Serve, Willing, Attitude, Worship, Joyful, Sing, Attendance Thanks, Time, Praise, Listen, Scripture, Offerings, Music, Communion

Worship the Lord

```
L  W  O  R  S  H  I  P  H  O  L
E  I  E  C  N  A  E  W  R  I  S
R  Y  S  W  O  T  R  A  E  H  R
U  S  I  T  P  T  G  H  I  O  N
T  L  N  W  E  E  E  E  L  F  D
P  U  G  E  O  N  D  M  T  F  G
I  F  D  J  B  D  U  I  H  E  N
R  Y  A  R  P  A  T  T  A  R  I
C  O  M  M  U  N  I  O  N  I  L
S  J  R  E  N  C  T  E  K  N  L
M  U  S  I  C  E  T  O  S  G  I
E  V  R  E  S  I  A  R  P  S  W
A  E  C  N  E  R  E  V  E  R  T
```

Come before Him with joyful singing—singing joyfully to the Lord is an act of worship.

Know that the LORD Himself is God—studying His Word and growing to know Him better is an act of worship.

We are His people—letting His Spirit direct our lives is an act of worship.

Enter His gates with thanksgiving—making church attendance a priority is an act of worship.

Give thanks to Him—taking time to thank Him is an act of worship.

Bless His name—praise is an act of worship.

More actions that are done during worship services are also acts of worship: Praying, listening (really listening not just hearing the words), reading Scripture, giving offerings, taking part in the music, participating in communion—all those are acts of worship.

Here's even more!

Your worship actually begins with your **preparation**—planning ahead so you aren't rushed or tempted to be angry or impatient with others, having a good attitude regardless of the circumstances, and making every effort to arrive on time. All these, too, are acts of worship.

Behavior—keeping silent while others speak or at times when silence is appropriate, being kind and hospitable to visitors, or paying attention and appreciating what others have done to put together the worship experience for you. These, too, are acts of worship.

And, **service**—being a part of the work that is needed to make a worship service possible is also worship, whether it takes place in the sanctuary or in some other part of the building.

Remember: **Worship is a matter of Heart**, but it is demonstrated by visible actions. God is worthy of worship; worship Him in spirit and in truth!

Rest and Reflect:

Think about a worship service you have attended and list out all the things that someone had to do to make that experience possible.

List some of the specific ways you can worship the Lord.

Improving Your Road

Memorize John 4:24.

Remember there are lots of ways to worship the Lord, and God welcomes them all—as long as they are done with a heart of worship.

Plan several special ways that you can worship the Lord in the weeks ahead.

ROAD
CONSTRUCTION
GUIDE

The Apostle's Doctrine
(...Hearing the Word of the Lord)

Acts 2:42
They were continually devoting themselves to the apostles' teaching and to fellowship, to the breaking of bread and to prayer.

Acts 2:42 tells us that the early Christians gathered together regularly to listen to the apostle's teaching. *Apostle's teaching* today would be the same as the preacher's sermon or a Sunday School teacher's lesson. The Apostles were teaching the new believers what Jesus had taught to them and what the Holy Spirit continued to teach them.

What did the Apostles actually teach?

Remember when the Church began the only Scripture that was written down was the Hebrew Scripture—our Old Testament. Within the next seventy years the gospels, the letters of the apostles, and the books of Acts and Revelation were finally available, too.

What does it mean to "Hear the Word"?

Hearing the Word means more than just hearing with your ears; it means **listening** intently to the words and trying to apply them to your life. Besides Sunday School and

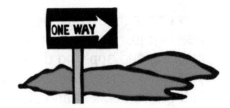

Find the Verse. Complete the blanks:
After Jesus called the crowd to Him, He said to them,
"_____ and

_____.
Matthew 15:10

Worship services, you can also *hear the Word* by taking part in small group Bible studies, attending Christian conferences, listening to Christian music, or paying attention when an older Christian shares what he or she has learned from God's Word.

Where do Christians today *hear the Word of the Lord*?

Christians today also need to continually meet to listen to more mature Christians teach from the Word of God. This is one of the important reasons to make *going to church* a priority.

Remember though, **listening to the preaching of the Word does not take the place of studying it for yourself**. Personal Bible Study is more than just reading the Bible; it is STUDYING THE BIBLE so you understand, remember, and apply the lessons you learn.

II Timothy 2:15 says that a believer is to **be diligent** about studying the Word.

What does that really mean? Reading is like hearing; just as you can *hear* without really listening and applying the words to your life, you can also *read* the Word without really letting them sink in and affect your life.

God wants us to **STUDY His Word**. That means that we need to read it, dig into it, understand it, and apply it to our lives.

Let's look closer at Paul's instructions to Timothy in II Timothy 2:15, "Be diligent to present yourself approved to God as a

---

Bible Study Tips:

Begin your study time by praying for wisdom and understanding of the words you will study.

Look up words you don't know in a dictionary.

Look up the verse in several different translations.

Break the verses apart into phrases and first study them. Then look at the whole verse or passage.

Rewrite verses or passages in your own words.

Ask yourself how you can apply the verse or passage to your life.

Keep a journal of your favorite verses. After each, write a few sentences about what it means to you.

---

workman who does not need to be ashamed, accurately handling the word of truth." Paul is essentially saying that we need to be diligent in the way we learn to handle God's Word so that when we come before the Lord, we will not have to be ashamed by our effort.

What are some ways a young believer can Study the Bible?

Some activities that may help you study the Bible include:

- Be consistent in your study—regularly study the Bible instead of just opening it up once in a while.
- Pray that the Holy Spirit will help you to understand what you read in the Bible.
- Read Scripture aloud.
- Use a dictionary to learn the meaning of words you don't understand.
- Study the maps in your Bible to see where the events took place.
- Learn to use a Bible Commentary and a Bible Concordance.
- Choose a topic and study all the verses you find that refer to the topic. (A concordance can help you find the verses.)
- Write verses out in your own words.
- Explain to someone else what you think a passage means.
- Do puzzles that use Bible verses or concepts.

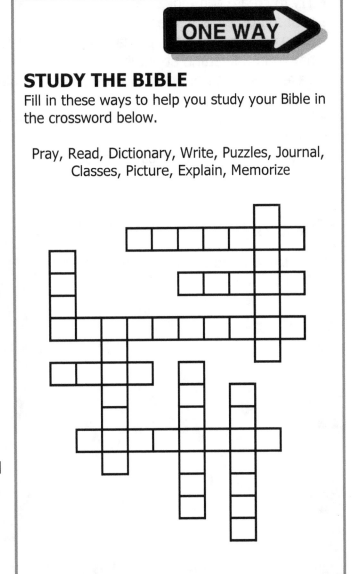

ONE WAY

STUDY THE BIBLE

Fill in these ways to help you study your Bible in the crossword below.

Pray, Read, Dictionary, Write, Puzzles, Journal, Classes, Picture, Explain, Memorize

• Try to create some puzzles of your own that are based on Bible Verses.

• Keep a journal—read a passage and write out what you understand about it.

• Take advantage of opportunities to go to Bible classes.

• Draw a picture that helps you visualize what is written.

• Memorize verses or passages of Scripture.

Draw a picture illustrating Psalm 23:1-3

Good Verses to memorize:

Deut. 6:5
John 14:15
Heb. 13:1
Prov. 15:1
John 14:1
Luke 6:31
I Corin. 15:33
Phil. 2:14
Phil. 3:14
James 1:22
Eph. 4:32
Gal. 6:9
Lam. 3:22-23
Rom. 8:37
II Corin. 12:9
Rom. 12:18
Phil. 4:4
II Thess. 3:13
Psalm 46:1
James 1:19
Prov. 3:5-6
Matt. 11:28
I Pet. 5:7
Phil. 4:19
James 1:5
Heb. 13:8
Matt. 6:33
Matt. 7:7
Matt. 22:37

Rest and Reflect:

What's the difference between just *hearing* the Word and actually *studying* the Word?

What are some ways that you can use to study the Bible?

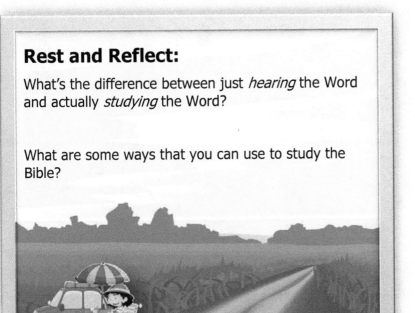

Improving Your Road

Memorize Timothy 2:15.

Plan to read and study your Bible for at least 20 minutes every day.

The Lord's Table
(...Why celebrate communion)

I Corinthians 11:26
For as often as you eat this bread and drink the cup, you proclaim the Lord's death until He comes.

Let's look at Acts 2:42 again. Another reason the Church met each week was to *break bread* together. This practice is what the Church now calls *communion*.

What is communion?

Communion is a celebration—a time of remembering that Jesus gave His life to provide salvation for everyone.

The practice of communion involves two primary components: eating a type of bread which represents the body of Christ and drinking grape juice which represents

NAMES FOR COMMUNION
Fill in the names used to refer to communion in the crossword below.

Bread, Cup, Breaking (of Bread), Supper (Lord's), Table (Lord's) Eucharist, Communion

the blood of Christ. (Wine is used in some churches.)

What are other names for communion?

Many names are given to the practice of communion.

Because of the elements involved, it is sometimes called *the bread and the cup* or *the breaking of bread*.

Because the elements are generally set upon a table and then ceremoniously distributed to the believers, it is sometimes referred to as *the Lord's Supper* or *the Lord's Table*.

More formally, it is referred to as a *sacrament* (a sacred act of the Church), and in some churches is called the *Eucharist*. (Eucharist is a Middle English term that is derived from Anglo-French, Latin, and Greek terms that all relate in some manner to gratitude.)

Who instituted it and when?

On the night that He was arrested, Jesus met with His disciples for one last Passover meal. At one point during that meal Jesus broke the matzo (the unleavened bread) and gave a piece to each of the disciples, telling them that it was to represent His body. He also shared a cup of wine, telling the disciples that it represented His blood.

Jesus told them that they were to eat the bread and drink the cup **in remembrance of Him**. So, Jesus instituted the ceremony!

Why should we take part in communion?

Jesus commanded all believers to do that

Build new words!
Write at least 10 words, with at least 4 letters, using only the letters in the word below.

COMMUNION

(communion) in remembrance of Him.

In I Corinthians 11:26, Paul explained why the Church was to continue the regular practice of communion. He wrote, "For as often as you eat this bread and drink the cup, you proclaim the Lord's death until He comes." That means that whenever you take part in communion you are again **taking a stand** with Christ, saying that He died for you and that someday He is coming back again.

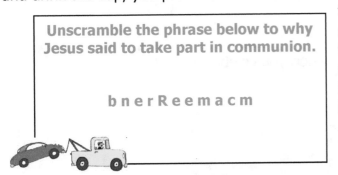

Unscramble the phrase below to why Jesus said to take part in communion.

b n e r R e e m a c m

How often should we take part in communion?

Acts 2:42 tells us the believers met every week and that each time they met, they remembered Jesus through the *breaking of bread.*

Remember: Communion is an act of obedience to the command of Christ. This, too, is an act of worship.

Rest and Reflect:

How often did the early church celebrate communion?

What are you actually doing when you celebrate communion?

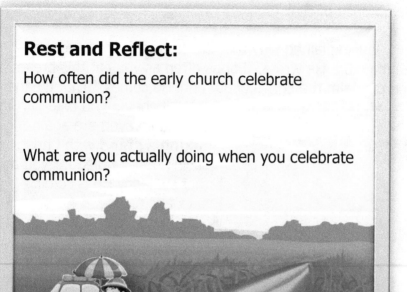

Improving Your Road

Memorize I Corinthians 11:26.

Remember that communion is not an empty ritual. It is a moment of re-aligning yourself to the Journey you have begun.

Examine yourself each time that you take part in communion. Rededicate yourself to Christ and renew your commitment to Him.

It's Not about Money
(...Giving offerings to the Lord)

II Corinthians 9:7
Each one must do just as he has purposed in his heart, not grudgingly or under compulsion, for God loves a cheerful giver.

Giving is one of the observable characteristics of a Christian—giving of self, giving of time, giving of talents, and YES, giving of money.

The Christian's approach to giving should always be based in two absolute truths:
- Everything we have belongs to God; we are His stewards (caretakers).
- Our giving is a response to our gratitude for what He has done for us.

Does God need money?

STOP

WRITE THIS DOWN: What does 10% look like? Draw 10 circles. Color nine of the circles blue and color one of them red. The red circle represents 10 %.

The Israelites were required to give a tithe (10%) of their income (generally crops and animals) to God. The Bible tells us that the praise/thanksgiving that was being presented in the offerings went to God, but most of the actual offerings themselves went to provide for the Levites. The Levites were the servants of the tabernacle or the temple; they owned no land of their own, so the offerings to God provided their income.

Thus, the offerings of the people served to show God their love and appreciation, but more practically, the gifts made it possible for God's physical work on earth to be accomplished.

DISCIPLESHIP IS A JOURNEY

The same is true today. God created the Church to carry on His work on earth until Jesus returns. Offerings to the church make that possible.

So, NO, God does not need our money, since He owns everything; but YES, His Church needs offerings and gifts to carry out the work He left to be done.

Find the words listed below in the grid of letters. Words may be up, down, or diagonal. They may also be spelled forward or backward.

Uses of Offerings

```
A T O W E L S C T N O
M S N O S S E L W N M
I U F L I C N E P I A
S S S Y O R W A T E R
S E E I S E C N G H K
I I F L C H A I R S E
O R O L B C Y N I K R
N E O A S A N G W U S
S T D O M E T G L U E
Y T I C I R T C E L E
E A N I B P A P E R Z
W B I B L E S S G U R
```

Batteries   Glue   Pencil
Bibles   Lessons   Preacher
Chairs   Markers   Rugs
Cleaning   Missions   Table
Electricity   Music   Towels
Food   Paper   Water

What does the church do with the money it receives?

To carry on the work of sharing the gospel and making disciples, the church needs **people** and **supplies**. Expenses for a church may include salaries for paid staff, utilities and furniture for a church building, and supplies for all the different activities that are held. Churches also often share part of the money it collects with missionaries who are also sharing the gospel of Christ.

Just like a family, churches have regular expenses that must be paid. That is why it is important for the congregation to contribute in a **consistent** manner, so the expenses can be paid.

How much should you give?

The early Christians gave out of gratitude for what God had done for them. They gave **generously** and with **a cheerful heart**.

Giving to the Lord is one more way that we show God how much we appreciate Him. Remember: Giving is a **choice**; it is an action that flows out of a grateful heart.

Giving is another act of worship!

When should you give?

Paul told the Corinthian church to gather their gifts for the Macedonian churches before He got there, so that when he arrived the gift would already be prepared. (II Corinthians 9: 5)

He also told them that each person should decide ahead of time what he wanted to give and then to proceed to give it. (II Corinthians 9:7)

So, what do Paul's instructions mean now? They mean that *giving* is not to be haphazard and impulsive. It is not just a one-time reaction to a worthy cause. Instead, it should be **regular and consistent**. It should be a thoughtful expression of your trust and gratitude.

Is giving more than just giving money?

Giving to the Lord is first about attitude and gratitude! Then, it is about giving money, time, and service.

The story of the Widow's Mite
(Mark 12:41-44)

Mark told of a time when Jesus watched as people brought their money to the temple. Many rich people gave lots of money, but an old widow put in only two small copper coins. Jesus said this woman gave more than all the rich people. Why? Because she gave all she had—not for show, but because she loved God.

Remember: Giving is a matter of the Heart!

Rest and Reflect:

Does God need your money?

Does God want you to cheerfully offer part of your money to your church?

How does the church use your offerings?

Improving Your Road

Memorize II Corinthians 9:7.

Decide something that you will offer to the Lord and then give the offering.

Discipleship Checkpoint

(If *Discipleship Is a Journey* is being used as a mentoring course, review the 4 prior lessons and discuss them with your mentor/counselor.)

Describe Worship and give some examples.

Describe ways that you can study God's Word. Why is it important to study the Bible?

Why is it important to celebrate communion regularly?

Why is giving to the Lord important? What should you give to the Lord?

TRAVELING DISCIPLESHIP ROAD
Understanding the role of service in a Christian's life

Discipleship is a lifelong journey; it does not stop when we get older. At different stages of life, the *road* looks different, but there are general *duties* that we need to always be doing. This section reviews some of the primary *jobs* that are expected of Christ's disciples.

 Not Just a List
(...Showing faith by your works)

 Growing a Servant's Heart
(...Serving others in love)

 Not Just Apples and Oranges
(...Exhibiting all the fruit of the Spirit)

 Cheering Others On
(...Encouraging others)

Not Just a List
(...Showing faith by your works)

James 2: 18
But someone may well say, "You have faith and I have works; show me your faith without the works, and I will show you my faith by my works."

Christianity is not a religion of Checklists. **No amount of good deeds** can earn a person a place in heaven.

The only **work** involved in the act of salvation is that which is done by God. Jesus, the Son of God, died and rose again so you could claim that gift of salvation through **faith**.

Remember Ephesians 2:8, "For by grace you have been saved through faith; and that not of yourselves, it is a gift of God." **Grace** says that God gave you what you did not deserve and **faith** says that you trust Him enough to accept it.

What is Faith, again?

Faith is complete trust or confidence in someone or something. Hebrews 11:1 says that faith is "the assurance of things hoped for, the conviction of things not seen." That means that even though you can't see God, you trust Him.

Find the Verse. Complete the blanks:
For by _____ you have been saved through _____; and that not of yourselves, it is a _____ of God... Ephesians 2:8

Faith is a **choice** that is founded on believing and on trusting. It is through faith that you believed in Christ and accepted His gift of salvation.

Where do *Works* fit in the picture of salvation?

Works are **actions** that are taken. A *work* is something that can be seen or measured. *Works* are a response to your faith; they are **evidence that your life has been changed**. They are evidence that the Holy Spirit is now living inside you.

Using 1=A, 2=B, etc. decode Titus 2:11 for another assurance of God's grace.

6 15 18   20 8 5

7 18 1 3 5   15 6   7 15 4

8 1 19   1 16 16 5 1 18 5 4,

2 18 9 14 7 9 14 7

19 1 12 22 1 20 9 15 14

20 15   1 12 12   13 5 14,...

So, what kinds of actions might show that you are a *new creation*? Some possibilities include: going to church regularly, giving to the church, studying the Bible, telling others about Jesus, being obedient to your parents, being kind to others, helping others whenever you can, and so forth. That kind of sounds like a checklist, doesn't it?

It's not really—a checklist implies a list of specific tasks to be done; what we are looking at here is not specific tasks, but rather a desire that "something" is done that shows evidence of God's presence in our lives.

Well, let's go back James 2:18.

James says, "show me your faith without the work." He means that you can't SEE faith if there are no works present.

Then he says, "I will show you my faith by my works," meaning that his works are evidence that there is faith present in his life.

So, works did not lead to your salvation, but works show that the salvation took place.

Are Works important, then?

Absolutely! Works are the visual signs that you have been saved. They are milestones along your Discipleship Journey.

Everyday your only "Checklist" (your plan of action) should be:
I am doing my best to learn what God wants me to do.
I am doing my best to obey God.
I am doing my best to grow to be like Jesus.

Any works that will help you accomplish that "Checklist" are worthy works to do.

Build new words!
Write at least 10 words, with at least 4 letters each, using only the letters in the word below.

FAITH WORKS

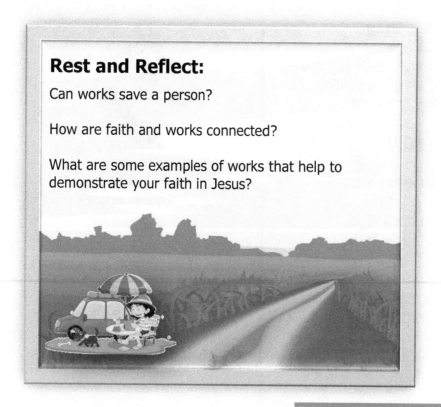

Rest and Reflect:

Can works save a person?

How are faith and works connected?

What are some examples of works that help to demonstrate your faith in Jesus?

Improving Your Road

Memorize Ephesians 2:8.

Make a list of special things you want to do this week to demonstrate your love for the Lord and then work on accomplishing them all.

Growing a Servant's Heart
(...Serving others in love)

Colossians 3:23-24
*Whatever you do, do your work heartily, as for the Lord rather than for men,
knowing that from the Lord you will receive the reward of the inheritance.
It is the Lord Christ whom you serve.*

The outward evidence of a Christian's inward relationship with Jesus is **service**.
(Service is one of the **works** that gives evidence of your faith.)

Jesus said, in Matthew 20:28 and in Mark 10:45, that He came into the world to
serve. To be like Christ is to be a servant—to have a **servant's heart**.

What does it mean to have a servant's heart?

A servant's heart is one that **wants to serve**, one that seeks to be able to
recognize the needs of others and then willingly tries to meet those needs.

The evidence of a servant's heart is not **what** the hands are doing, **where** the
feet are going, or **who** is receiving the service. The measure of the servant's
heart is not in the importance of the service or even whether it
is noticed by others.

The key to having a servant's heart is in the **attitude**—the
understanding that your service to others is actually a gift you
are giving to God. In Colossians 3:23-24, Paul reminded the
believers that anything they did for others was actually being
done for Christ.

Is any service too small?

In Matthew 25:40 Jesus told a parable about service. In the end He said, "Truly I say to you, to the extent that you did it to one of these brothers of Mine, even the least of them, you did it to me."

No service is too small. It's not about what you do; it's about **why** you do it. Do everything for the Lord.

STOP THIS DOWN: Make a list of small acts of service you could do without calling attention to your actions.

Using 1=A, 2=B, etc. decode Ephesians 6:7, another verse that encourages service to the Lord.

23 9 20 8   7 15 15 4

23 9 12 12   18 5 14 4 5 18

19 5 18 22 9 3 5   1 19

20 15   20 8 5   12 15 18 4

1 14 4   14 15 20   20 15

13 5 14,...

What ways can I serve others?

Service means **action**—doing something. Serving others requires that you make a choice to give up your time, energy, or possessions to benefit someone else.

There are many, many ways that Christians serve one another—and any of them is pleasing to the Lord.

Does serving mean committing?

Remember the "works" mentioned in the prior section? Serving others is a visual sign that tells others you are a disciple of Christ.

In Matthew 5:16 Jesus said, "Let your light shine before men in such a way that they may see your good works, and glorify your Father who is in heaven." That means that all the little things you do for others point people to Jesus.

So, are we just checking off acts of service? No, having a servant's heart is more than doing a haphazard collection of small acts for others; it is a lifestyle—it is a commitment to making **service to others** a priority in our lives.

What if I don't FEEL like serving?

You cannot always trust your feelings because emotions and feelings change with the circumstances. Discouragement and disappointment, or even pride and selfishness can influence feelings, but service comes out of a faithful, committed **choice** to obey the calling of Christ.

Paul reminds believers in Galatians 6:9, "Let us not lose heart in doing good, for in due time we will reap if we do not grow weary." That means—**Don't give up** on serving the Lord!

When you just don't *feel like* doing good, choose to ACT on the commitment that you already made. Soon, your **feelings** will catch up to your **choice**, as you continue to honor God with your service.

Build new words!
Write at least 10 words, with at least 4 letters, using only the letters in the word below.

COMMITMENT

Is service worship?

Absolutely! Serving others is one of the purest forms of worship! When you choose to serve others **because** you love God, you are giving Him a precious gift—you are letting Him know that what He values is important to you, too.

Rest and Reflect:

What does it mean to have a servant's heart?

When you don't *feel like* serving, should you just stop serving?

What does it mean to be committed to serving others?

Improving Your Road

Memorize Colossians 3:23-24.

Service to others is often one of the *works* that demonstrates our love and faith.

Make a list of special ways you can serve the church or serve others and plan to do them soon.

Not Just Apples and Oranges
(...Exhibiting all the fruit of the Spirit)

Galatians 5:22-23
But the fruit of the Spirit is love, joy, peace, patience, kindness, goodness, faithfulness, gentleness, self-control; against such things there is no law.

When you were baptized, the Holy Spirit came to live inside you. He came to help you **learn** what God wants you to do and to help you **remember** what you have learned. He came to comfort you when you need comforting and encourage you when you are weary or fearful.

But, beyond God's promise that He would come, how do you know He's there?

We know He is there because we see changes in our lives; we see **evidence** of His presence. What evidence?

Let's look at an apple tree. If you see a tree, how can you tell that it is an apple tree? You recognize it is an apple tree by its fruit. You don't find oranges on an apple tree. You find apples on an apple tree!

Fruit of the Spirit: Draw an apple tree with apples on it.

And you recognize that the Holy Spirit is in you by seeing the *fruit of the Spirit* in your life.

What is the fruit of the Spirit?

The *fruit of the Spirit* are the characteristics that demonstrate the presence of the Holy Spirit. As you study God's Word and strive to serve Him, the Holy Spirit helps you begin to become like Him—loving, kind, patient, etc. That is the fruit of the Spirit. It is the ongoing molding of your character to help you become like Jesus.

So what characteristics does the Holy Spirit help you to demonstrate? They are listed in Galatians 5:22-23.

Love, Joy, Peace, Patience, Kindness, Goodness, Faithfulness, Gentleness, Self-control

Is it All or Nothing?

The reference in Galatians says *fruit* not fruits. Is that intentional? Can you strive for Love and Joy and not worry about being Patient or Kind?

ONE WAY

FRUIT OF THE SPIRIT

Fill in the Fruit of the Spirit in the crossword below.

Love, Joy, Peace, Patience, Kindness, Goodness, Faithfulness, Gentleness, Self-Control

Remember: the fruit of the Spirit is referring to the **character of God** that the Holy Spirit is helping you to develop. There is no separating the traits—they are all bound together in His character, much like many kinds of fruit are mixed together to form a fruit salad.

So, NO, you can't pick and choose which ones you want. The Holy Spirit is molding your life to demonstrate all of God's characteristics—**all** of His character.

Remember, though, you are on a Journey. God's not done yet. On any particular day, some part of the fruit of the Spirit may be more apparent than other parts.

STOP

WRITE THIS DOWN:
For each fruit of the Spirit listed below, name one thing you can to demonstrate it in your own life.

LOVE

_____

JOY

_____

PEACE

_____

PATIENCE

_____

KINDNESS

_____

GOODNESS

_____

FAITHFULNESS

_____

GENTLENESS

_____

SELF-CONTROL

_____

What does having the fruit of the Spirit in my life look like?

Let's look at the various characteristics that the Spirit is helping you develop.

Love
The mark of Christ-like love in your life is that you love unconditionally. You love people without expecting to receive anything in return.

Joy
Having joy is based on having Christ in your life. Your happiness does not depend on whether things are going smoothly for you.

Peace
Philippians 4:7 says that the peace of God that surpasses all comprehension will guard your

heart. Even in the middle of trouble or uncertainties, you can remain calm in the assurance of His presence.

Patience
Having patience means that you are not easily irritated with others because you try to see them as God sees them. It also means that you understand that God's timing is difference than yours and you are content to wait for when He chooses to answer your prayers.

Kindness
Ephesians 4:32 describes being kind as being tender-hearted and forgiving of one another. Kindness is seen in the desire to serve others.

Goodness
Goodness is demonstrated when you make choices or do good works that help others to know Jesus better.

Faithfulness
Faithfulness implies a continuing, unshakable assurance that comes from your reliance on God.

Draw lines matching the fruit with a description of each.

	Doing good works
Love	
Joy	Continuing to follow
	Calm assurance even in the midst of troubles
Peace	
Patience	Unconditional regard for others
Kindness	
	Not easily angered or quarrelsome
Goodness	
Faithfulness	Not expecting immediate answers
Gentleness	Happiness not dependent on circumstances
Self-Control	
	Tenderhearted, forgiving
	Allowing the Holy Spirit to lead you

Gentleness

Gentleness is demonstrated in a likeable disposition, one that is not easily angered or quarrelsome.

Self-control

Self-control refers not to letting yourself be in charge, but to controlling yourself, so that the Holy Spirit can lead you.

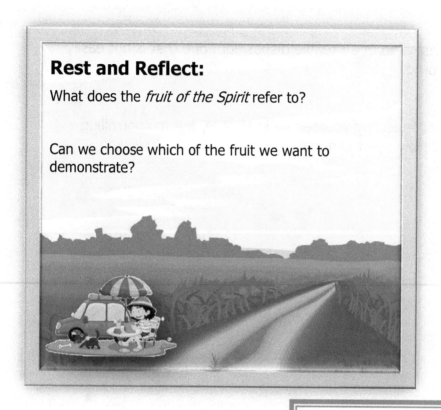

Rest and Reflect:

What does the *fruit of the Spirit* refer to?

Can we choose which of the fruit we want to demonstrate?

Improving Your Road

Memorize Galatians 5:22-23.

Make a list of the fruit of the Spirit. Think about Christians you know who demonstrate these fruit. Talk to some of those Christians about the fruit of the Spirit and ask them if they have any suggestions that would help you grow in your relationship with the Lord. Let them know that you appreciate the example they have shown you.

ROAD CONSTRUCTION GUIDE

Cheering Others On
(...Encouraging others)

I Thessalonians 5:11
*Therefore encourage one another and build up one another,
just as you also are doing.*

Sometimes circumstances of life are hard to understand and hard to endure. Problems seem too large to handle. Disappointments try to steal a believer's faith.

One of God's answers to those times is **Encouragement**—one Christian encouraging another.

Remember: your Journey is yours alone, but many believers share the road. God uses the Church to win the lost, but also to encourage one another.

What is encouragement?

Encouragement is giving someone confidence or hope. It is motivating or inspiring someone by reminding them that they have value.

Build new words!
Write at least 10 words, with at least 4 letters each, using only the letters in the word below.

ENCOURAGEMENT

Encouragement is like an **invisible crutch**. It helps a person to stand, when he would be too weak to do so without help.

How do I encourage others?

The act of encouraging others requires little from you, except your heart. The simple purpose of encouragement is to **remind** the other person that they are not alone and that someone (God and His followers) cares about them.

Small gifts, cards, or even a hug or a smile can be used to encourage someone. But, mostly encouragement uses Words!

• Words that remind the believer of God's presence
• Words that remind him of the faithfulness of God
• Words that let the believer know that people love him
• Words that let him know people are praying for him
• Words that let him know people believe in him
• Words that let him know you trust him
• Words that remind him that he can hold on and he can keep moving forward
• Words that inspire him be strong in his faith

Using 1=A, 2=B, etc. decode Galatians 6:2 to learn another way to encourage one another.

2 5 1 18   15 14 5

1 14 15 20 8 5 18' 19

2 21 18 4 5 14 19   1 14 4

20 8 5 18 5 2 25   6 21 12 6 9 12 12

20 8 5   12 1 23   15 6

3 8 18 9 19 20.

Words are a very powerful tool. **Never underestimate the power of encouragement!**

Why should I encourage others?

Read I Thessalonians 5:11 again! Does it sound optional? No, it is commanded of all who seek to be like Christ.

Remember: The Church is the body of Christ. Every believer is a part of that body. Also, when one member of the body hurts, the whole body is affected. We encourage one another **so that the whole body can be made stronger**.

How can I encourage?

Let's be practical. What are some ways you can encourage others in their own Discipleship Journeys?

Encourage others by **sharing pieces of God's Word**. Let Scripture—the Word of God—fill their hearts with peace, so they can grow stronger in their faith.

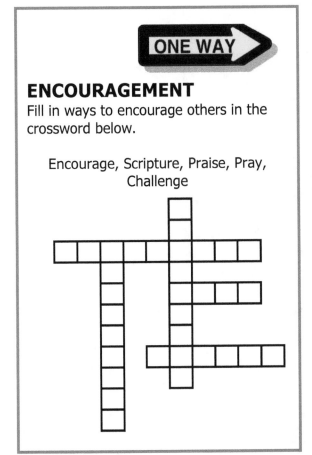

ENCOURAGEMENT
Fill in ways to encourage others in the crossword below.

Encourage, Scripture, Praise, Pray, Challenge

• John 14:27 - He has given us peace unlike any the world can offer.
• John 16:33 - He has overcome the world.
• Psalm 120:1 - Call on Him in distress and He will answer.
• I Peter 5:7 - Cast your anxiety on Him because He cares for you.

Praise their accomplishments or recognize the good things they have done. Point out strengths you see in them. Take notice of the good things they do, and let them know you noticed. Offer honest, genuine praise, not empty flattery.

Pray for them. Let them know you are praying.

Challenge them to try harder. Let them know you believe they are capable of doing great things.

Rest and Reflect:

What is encouragement?

List some practical ways you can encourage others.

Improving Your Road

Memorize I Thessalonians 5:11.

Encourage at least 4 people this week.

Plan to send an encouragement note to someone every week this month.

Discipleship Checkpoint

(If *Discipleship Is a Journey* is being used as a mentoring course, review the 4 prior lessons and discuss them with your mentor/counselor.)

How are faith and works related in regard to your salvation?

What does it mean to have a servant's heart?

Name the fruit of the Spirit. How can you demonstrate them in your life?

Explain ways that you can encourage others.

THE ROAD WINDS ON
Understanding that Discipleship is a lifelong journey

The *relationship* between God and the Christian does not end. As our journey continues, we look forward to the time when we will go to heaven to be with God. This section reviews a few final concepts every Christian should keep in mind as he waits for Jesus to return.

Get Back Up
(...It's OK to stumble)

Don't Travel Alone
(...Sharing your faith with others)

Rough Road Ahead
(...Understanding that problems will come)

Don't Close the Book Yet
(...Continue learning and growing)

Get Back Up
(...It's OK to stumble)

I John 1:9
If we confess our sins, He is faithful and righteous to forgive us our sins and to cleanse us from all unrighteousness.

When you were baptized, your sins were washed away. You were forgiven — totally—past, present, and future. Jesus' death on the cross paid for ALL your sin. You became a new creature; the Holy Spirit came into your heart to be by your side ALWAYS.

As a new Christian, you began your Discipleship Journey with a brand new, CLEAN, heart. All Sin was gone from your life.

WRITE THIS DOWN:
Write the if/then promise found in I John 1:9.

The first step was perfect—what happened?

Does the fact that you are forgiven mean you are perfect? Does it mean that you will never sin again?

NO! You still have the same human body, the same human nature, and the same human tendency to put **Self** before God. AND, you still have **free will** to make your own choices! So, yes, you will sin again, you will fail to obey God's commands.

But, God's love covers that too. WHEN, you stumble; WHEN you fail to be faithful to God's commands, He is still there and His forgiveness still stands. You are forgiven!

What do you do when you sin again?

Read I John 1:9. "If we confess our sins, He is faithful and righteous to forgive us our sins and to cleanse us from all unrighteousness."

Now READ it again.

Notice God's promise—*If we confess our sins* then He (God) will forgive us. He has forgiven you. He has promised to help you to not sin again. AND He has promised to continue forgiving you as long as you continue asking for that forgiveness.

But, why must you confess again?

If He has already promised that the sin is forgiven, why must you still confess and ask for forgiveness?

Think about it! God knows you sin. God knows He has already forgiven that sin. The real question is: **Do YOU know you have sinned?** Unless you recognize you have sinned, and admit it (to yourself), you cannot understand that you need to stop doing the sin.

That is why *confessing your sin* is important. When you confess your sin and ask God to forgive you, what you are really doing it telling God that **you realize you have failed AGAIN** and that you want to accept His forgiveness again so you can get on with your Discipleship Journey again.

Will God ever give up on you?

Read I John 1:9 AGAIN!

Notice: "He is faithful and righteous to forgive us our sins and to cleanse us from all unrighteousness."

Faithfulness is a part of God's character. God loves you. He is faithful. He will never give up on you!

What are some actions that will help you avoid sinning?

Remember: Sin is **anything** that is against the will or the command of God.

Using 1=A, 2=B, etc. decode II Timothy 2:13 to learn another reason God won't give up on you.

9 6   23 5   1 18 5

6 1 9 20 8 12 5 19 19,   8 5

18 5 13 1 9 14 19

6 1 9 20 8 6 21 12,   6 15 18

8 5   3 1 14 14 15 20

4 5 14 25   8 9 13 19 5 12 6.

The psalmist asked, "How can a young man keep his way pure?" and then answered his own question, "By keeping it according to Your word." (Psalm 119:9)

To keep from sinning:
> Continue to study God's Word and apply it to your life.
> Continue to fellowship with other Christians.
> Continue to be actively involved in the Church.
> Continue to pray for the guidance of the Holy Spirit.
> Continue to serve others in the name Jesus.
> Continue your Discipleship Journey.

Again, what do you do when you sin?

As a disciple of Jesus your desire should always be to **faithfully** continue your Discipleship Journey. You should strive to always be obedient. You should strive to never sin again.

But, when you fail; when you stumble: Confess your sin to the Lord, **get up**, and **continue** your Discipleship journey!

Rest and Reflect:

Will you still sin after your baptism?

If you do sin again, what should you do?

What can you do to help you continue to be faithful and obedient to God's commands?

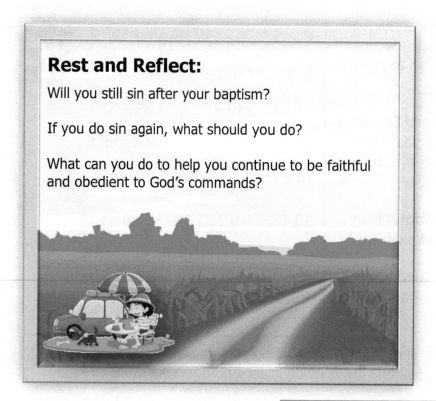

Improving Your Road

Memorize I John 1:9.

Ask a trusted Christian friend to continue to pray for you to keep following the ways of the Lord.

Continue to pray for your friends to also be strong in their Discipleship Journeys.

Don't Travel Alone
(...Sharing your faith with others)

Matthew 28:19-20
*Go therefore and make disciples of all the nations, baptizing them
in the name of the Father and the Son and the Holy Spirit,
teaching them to observe all that I commanded you;
and lo, I am with you always, even to the end of the age.*

Each Discipleship Journey is unique because it is a personal journey that the disciple shares with Jesus. But, you are not alone. Other believers, who are on their own Discipleship Journeys, share the road with you.

The journeys of all the believers form what is kind of like a **spiritual caravan**. We are all traveling the same road, each in our separate vehicles. Together, we all carry out the work of the Church as we follow Christ.

What is the primary work of the Church again?

Simply put, they (the disciples) were to **Go**, **Make** disciples (more disciples), **Teach** those disciples to obey Christ's commands, and **Baptize** new believers.

In other words the primary job of the Church is to **tell others about Jesus so more people can accept Him**.

The Church as a whole refers to Matthew 28:19-20 as the **Great Commission**. A commission is a job or duty that is given by one who is in authority. The Church's commission is from Jesus. The job of the Church—the job of every believer who is a part of that Church—is to witness to others about Jesus.

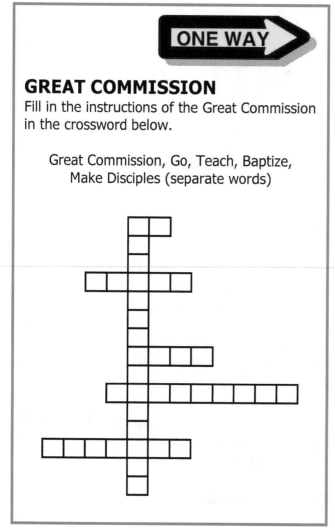

GREAT COMMISSION

Fill in the instructions of the Great Commission in the crossword below.

Great Commission, Go, Teach, Baptize, Make Disciples (separate words)

In Acts 22:15, Luke writes, "For you will be a witness for Him to all men of what you have seen and heard." In this verse Ananias is telling Paul what he is to do now that he had met Jesus on the road to Damascus. He was to witness (tell others) everything that he had seen and heard (about his experience with Jesus). **This is the same instruction that is given to all followers of Jesus.**

What is witnessing?

Witnessing is simply the **act of telling** someone else what you know—what you saw or heard. It does not have to be complicated. It is just sharing about who Christ is and what He has done for you.

Peter, one of Jesus' disciples, described the simple process in I Peter 3:15, "but sanctify Christ as Lord in your hearts, always **being ready** to make a defense to everyone who asks you to give an account for the hope that is in you, yet with gentleness and reverence."

What did Peter mean? Simply put, he was saying, "**First** make Christ Lord of your life; **then be ready** to explain why you are filled with hope whenever others notice that you are different."

That is what witnessing is all about. There is something special about a life filled with Christ. Witnessing is just explaining to others what causes the difference in your life.

How do you witness?

You witness **with your words** when you tell others about Jesus, invite them to go to church with you, offer help when it is needed, speak well of everyone, etc.

WRITE THIS DOWN: The key to witnessing to others is to

Be _____ to give an answer for the hope you have.

You witness **with your actions** when you help others with things that need to be done, share what you have with others, don't swear or use bad language, are kind and encouraging, are honest and trustworthy, etc.

You also witness **with your lifestyle** when you make going to church a priority, choose only good, moral forms of entertainment, etc.

What things are not witnessing?

Witnessing is not:
- Arguing about whose church is better or about what a Bible verse means
- Debating about Scripture or church history
- Trying to make someone feel guilty
- Ridiculing someone for what they believe or how they act
- Trying to force someone to make a decision

Unscramble some of the "Don'ts" of witnessing.

c f r o e   e e b d t a

e g a u r   u i i r d e c l

s u e u i g t l (2 words)

What if they won't listen?

The job of a witness is to report what they know. **Nothing more.**

Remember: the decision to follow Jesus is a **CHOICE** that everyone must make for themselves. Your job is not to make them make that choice; your job is to give them information they need to help them decide what their choice will be.

Rest and Reflect:

What does witnessing involve?

What are some of the don'ts of witnessing?

When should you be ready to share what God has done for you.

Improving Your Road

Memorize I Peter 3:15.

Write down three things God has done for you.

Be ready to share these with anyone who asks why your life seems different from others.

ROAD CONSTRUCTION GUIDE

Rough Road Ahead
(...Understanding that problems will come)

John 16:33
These things I have spoken to you, so that in Me you may have peace. In the world you have tribulation, but take courage; I have overcome the world.

Your Discipleship Journey will not always be straight and smooth. Christians face the same problems as everyone else!

Jesus never promised a smooth journey. In fact, He told His disciples that they would have tribulation in this world (John 16:33). He meant that they would have **problems**—things would not always be easy; things would not always go the way the disciples wanted them to go.

But Jesus also assured them, "I have overcome the world." That means that no matter how hard things get, God is **STILL** in charge!

Why do we have problems?

When God created the world, it was perfect. Then sin entered the world and with sin came pain and problems of all kinds.

Now, trouble is quite literally a **fact of life**.

Some problems are caused by the bad

> Using 1=A, 2=B, etc. decode Jesus' promise] to His followers.
>
> 9   1 13
>
> 23 9 20 8   25 15 21
>
> 1 12 23 1 25 19.

choices that have been made in the past, and some problems just exist because this world is corrupted.

What kind of problems?

Pain, Sickness,
Sadness, Loneliness, Disappointments, Discouragement
Loss or ruin of possessions
Failure to get what we want, Failure to achieve some goals
Difficulties with school, with jobs, with family members and friends
And more...

Problems come in all shapes and sizes, but two things are true of them all:
- They are **normal**. You are not the only one to ever face any particular problem.

- They are subject to the authority of God. **God is STILL in charge**. Never forget that with God's Spirit living in you, you are not facing your problems alone.

What should you do when things get rough?

Keep trusting.
Proverbs 3:5-6 says, "Trust in the LORD with all your heart and do not lean on your own understanding. In all your ways acknowledge Him, and He will make your paths straight."

Unscramble the words below to review what you should keep doing when troubles come into your life.

g e i s v r n,   u n s y t d i g,

n r y g p i a, & r n t t u i s g

Keep studying God's Word.
II Tim 2:15 says, "Be diligent to present yourself approved to God as a workman who does not need to be ashamed, accurately handling the word of truth."

Keep praying.
Colossians 4:2 says, "Devote yourselves to prayer, keeping alert in it with an attitude of thanksgiving."

Keep serving the Lord.
II Thessalonians 3:13 says, "But as for you, brethren, do not grow weary of doing good."

Lessons learned through problems.

Again, problems are a fact of life. Everyone faces them. But Christians understand that God can make use of every trial (problem) they encounter to help them become a better follower.

James 1:2-4 records, "**Consider** it all **joy**, my brethren, when you **encounter** various **trials**, knowing that the testing of your **faith** produces **endurance.** And let endurance have its perfect result, so that you may be perfect and **complete**, lacking nothing."

But, what did James mean?

Consider it all joy. Do you have to be happy that you have problems? Not happy to have the problems, but **happy** with what will come about because of the **problems**.

Find the RED "lessons" words in the grid. (Up, down, or diagonal; forward or backward)

Consider, Joy, Encounter, Trials, Faith Endurance, Complete, All Happy, Problems, Trust, Help, Relationship, Like, Perfect, Nothing

Approach to Problems

```
C E C N A R U D N E
Y O P R O B L E M S
R P S E T T U H D C
E E P L S A H E L P
D N I A M F A I T H
I C Y T H S O K N N
S O J I T R U S T G
N U C O M P L E T E
O N L N Y B K S A R
C T L S Y I N L Q W
R E A H L R G Y O V
W R I I S L A I R T
F J P P E R F E C T
```

DISCIPLESHIP IS A JOURNEY

Testing of your faith produces endurance. What does faith have to do with problems? Whenever you face a problem you have two choices—give up and let it overcome you or trust that God will help you get through it. Just like exercising strengthens your body's muscles, facing problems (and working through them with God's help) strengthens your faith.

So that you may be perfect and complete, lacking nothing. Is that really possible? Yes. As your faith and your relationship with Jesus grow, you become more like Him. With Him, you are perfect and complete and you need nothing else besides Him.

That is really what your Discipleship Journey is all about—following Jesus so you can become like Him.

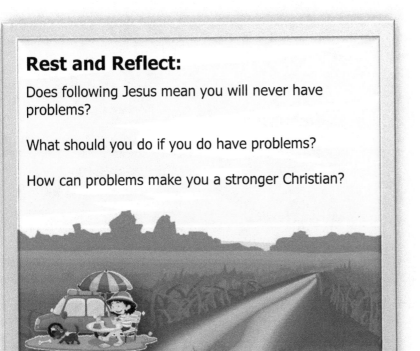

Rest and Reflect:

Does following Jesus mean you will never have problems?

What should you do if you do have problems?

How can problems make you a stronger Christian?

Improving Your Road

Memorize John 16:33.

On an index card, write a note to yourself, reminding yourself that God is STILL in charge, no matter what problems you face. Put the note somewhere you will see it frequently and reread it when you need to be reminded.

Don't Close the Book Yet
(...Continue learning and growing)

John 8:31
So Jesus was saying to those Jews who had believed Him, "If you continue in my Word, then you are truly disciples of Mine."

Remember: **Discipleship is a lifelong Journey**.

Keep on your Journey!

Discipleship—following Jesus—is ongoing. The key word in your journey is **Continue**!

Continue to study and learn His Word; **continue** to grow in faith; **continue** to serve His people, until He comes again.

What's at the end of the Journey?

WRITE THIS DOWN:

The key word in your Discipleship Journey is

_____!

Remember, AGAIN: Discipleship is a lifelong journey. It is a constant, consistent, building of the relationship with Christ. Though you look ahead to the time when you can be with Christ, the focus of your Discipleship Journey is on **the journey**—not on the end.

Nevertheless, let's look at just a couple things you will find when your journey is complete.

1. *Jesus*

Here on earth Jesus is *with you* through the presence of the Holy Spirit. When you have faithfully completed your journey, you will meet Him *face to face*. One day, Jesus will return, and all His disciples will live with Him forever.

2. *Heaven*

Heaven is the place where God dwells. Even now, the Father is sitting on His throne, with Jesus at His right hand.

Before Jesus left earth, He promised that He was going to prepare a place for us and that one day He would return. When He returns, we will live with Him forever in the wonderful place that He is preparing.

3. *Crowns*

Scripture describes several crowns or rewards that may be given to believers, based on their Discipleship Journeys.

Draw a picture of a crown you would like to receive someday.

Never confuse the promise of rewards with the gift of salvation! Your rewards are earned by your own actions; your salvation was purchased and delivered to you by Christ.

Let's look at some of the crowns you might one day have.

I Corinthians 9:24-25 says that believers who faithfully continue to follow Christ will receive **an incorruptible crown**—a crown that cannot be destroyed.

I Thessalonians 2:19-20 says that believers who faithfully witness about the saving grace of God will receive **the crown of rejoicing**.

II Timothy 4:8 says that **a crown of righteousness** will be given to all those who have *loved His appearing*. That means the crown is given to everyone who faithfully looks forward to His return.

James 1:2 says that **a crown of life** will be given to everyone who keeps on trusting all the way to the end of the journey.

I Peter 5:4 says that the Chief Shepherd (Jesus) will even give **an unfading crown of glory** to those who have faithfully helped others to come to know Him.

What, then, should we be doing?

Remember: **Discipleship is a lifelong journey**. The journey does not end until we go to be with Him.

Paul tells believers, in Philippians 3:13-15, to *press on*. In other words—**continue!**

Your Discipleship Journey began in the waters of baptism; it ends in the very presence of God!

Until then...
Continue to be His disciple;
Continue to study and learn His Word;
Continue to grow in faith;
Continue to serve His people.

Build new words!
Write at least 10 words, with at least 4 letters, using only the letters in the word below.

CONTINUE

Rest and Reflect:

How long is your Discipleship Journey?

When will it end?

What crowns might you receive?

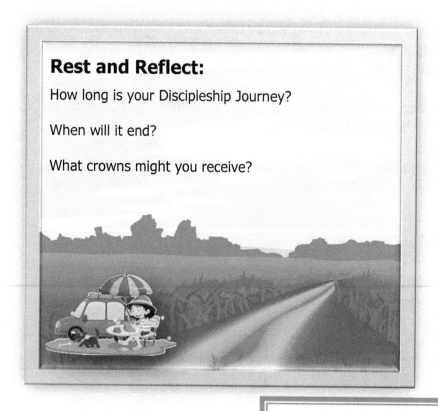

Improving Your Road

Memorize John 14:2-3.

Remember: Discipleship is a journey!

Commit yourself now to follow the way of the Lord daily.

Pray for strength and wisdom to be able to keep your commitment.

ENJOY the journey!

Discipleship Checkpoint

(If *Discipleship Is a Journey* is being used as a mentoring course, review the 4 prior lessons and discuss them with your mentor/counselor.)

When you fail to obey some of the commands of Jesus, what should you do?

What is witnessing? What part does it play in your Discipleship Journey?

Does following Jesus guarantee that we will never have problems? If we do have problems, how should we handle them?

When does your Discipleship Journey end? What should you do until it ends?